Ma

THE CHALLENGE OF CHEMISTRY

THE CHALLENGE OF CHEMISTRY

PHILIP A. HORRIGAN

CHAIRMAN
DEPARTMENT OF CHEMISTRY
SOUTHERN CONNECTICUT STATE COLLEGE

McGRAW-HILL BOOK COMPANY

NEW YORK   ST. LOUIS   SAN FRANCISCO
DÜSSELDORF   LONDON   MEXICO
PANAMA   SIDNEY   TORONTO

THE
CHALLENGE
OF
CHEMISTRY

Library of Congress Catalog Card Number 74-95808

30400

2 3 4 5 6 7 8 9 0   HDMM   7 9 8 7 6 5 4 3 2 1 0

This book was set in News Gothic
by Monotype Composition Company, Inc.,
printed on permanent paper by Halliday Lithograph Corporation,
and bound by The Maple Press Company.
The designer was J. Paul Kirouac;
the drawings were done by BMA Associates, Inc.
The editors were
James L. Smith, David A. Beckwith, and Maureen McMahon.
Adam Jacobs supervised the production.

TO JOHN C. BAILAR, JR.

PREFACE

Most people are not going to become great chemists—or even average chemists. But that should keep no one from sharing the excitement of a field which plays a vital role in today's society. I have tried, in the following chapters, to bring you an understanding of some of the fundamentals of chemistry, the activities of the chemist, the operation of a chemical research department, and the application of chemical principles to several popular topics of deep concern to us all.

There is another possibility that I have borne in mind in writing "The Challenge of Chemistry." A considerable number of non-science majors are, without their awareness, quite capable of pursuing a career in science. It often happens that a student in a chemistry survey course decides to follow a career in chemistry and becomes very successful.

It is my sincere hope that those of you who find chemistry forbidding will, after reading this book, have become aware of its fascination. And if some of you should decide to become chemists, I would be doubly rewarded.

PHILIP A. HORRIGAN

CONTENTS

THE CHALLENGE OF CHEMISTRY

1

GENERAL

Matter is composed of extremely small particles called atoms. Everything around us, including ourselves, is an arrangement of various atoms stuck together in a particular fashion. If we could know exactly how all these atoms are arranged, how they could be rearranged, and which properties are associated with each arrangement, our knowledge and accomplishments would be practically limitless. Diseases could be eliminated; the life process could be extended and improved; there would be almost no physical problem we could not solve. Therefore, it becomes important for us to study the atoms, their reactions, and the properties afforded by various atomic arrangements.

THEORY AND LAW

If the chemist prepares a structure involving four carbon atoms sur-sounding a nitrogen atom and observes that this produces a bactericidal

◀ PHOTO BY PERMISSION OF MUSEUM OF CONTEMPORARY CRAFTS, NEW YORK CITY.

action, then he makes other compounds with similar structures in the hope of developing a better bactericide or fungicide, or perhaps a new wonder drug. If the chemist finds that a certain chainlike arrangement of carbon atoms produces a clear, tough plastic material, he will prepare chain structures in search of other plastic materials with special properties, such as softness, flexibility, and durability.

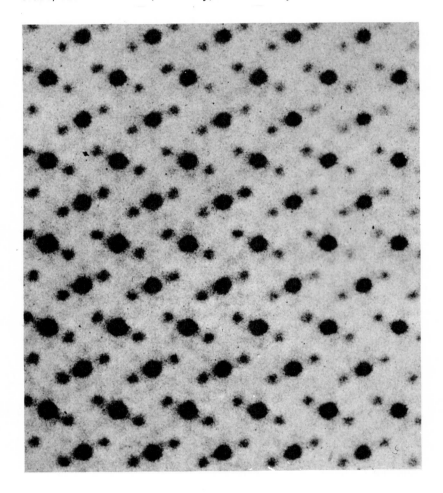

FIGURE 1–1   A CHIP OF THE MINERAL MARCASITE, MAGNIFIED ABOUT 40 MILLION TIMES. THE LARGER SPOTS ARE IRON ATOMS, THE SMALLER ONES ARE SULFUR ATOMS. (*COURTESY OF M. J. BUERGER.*)

The chemist, then, is studying the atoms, the combinations of various atoms (called compounds), their reactions, the structures they produce, and ultimately the properties exhibited by these structures. When he has accumulated a large amount of data on a particular topic, he often proposes a theory to explain what he observes. If other experimenters under various conditions make the same observations, the theory becomes a law. I must emphatically point out here that chemistry is an experimental science and that, in contrast to some fields of knowledge, such as history or geography in which essentially all the facts are known, the theories and laws of chemistry depend upon day-to-day observations in research laboratories throughout the world. What appears to be a solid theory today may, in the face of new data, have to be adjusted or even discarded tomorrow.

Let me give you an example of a scientific law that had to be changed. Not long ago one spoke of "the conservation of mass." (Mass is the amount of matter contained in an object. Weight is the force imposed on the object by the gravitational attraction of the earth. These two terms are often used interchangeably.) This meant that when a collection of atoms underwent some sort of reaction, you still had the same atoms after the reaction even though they were now in a different arrangement. Therefore, it was logical to assume that the mass of the atoms before and after reaction was the same, and we had the law of conservation of mass.

On the other hand, Albert Einstein predicted a mass and energy equivalence. Accordingly, when atoms undergo certain nuclear reactions (more about this later on) that release large amounts of energy, it is observed that the mass of the products is smaller than the mass of the starting atoms. The amount of energy released, however, is shown to be exactly equivalent to the amount of mass lost according to Einstein's mass-energy equivalence prediction. Chemists now believe that in ordinary

FIGURE 1–2

chemical reactions, which involve much less energy than nuclear reactions, there is also a change in mass, although an extremely small and undetectable one. The law has now been amended to the law of conservation of mass and energy. In other words, if we add together the energy and mass before reaction, their sum should exactly equal the sum of the energy and the mass after reaction.

SCIENTIFIC ATTITUDE

Before we start a discussion of the structure of the atom, let me point out one more very important fact. Atoms under a certain set of conditions will react a particular way, and if we repeat the experiment under *exactly* the same conditions, the atoms will behave the same way. If this were not so, we would have no science, no theories or laws, and there would be no point in recording any observations. Accordingly, the chemist must be very honest and objective in making observations. Under controlled conditions the atoms will not be influenced by the nationality of the observer, the time of day, or the desire of the researcher to go home early. The expression "scientific attitude" applies to an extremely objective state of mind, not influenced by anything but pertinent physical observations. If a compound turns out to be blue when it should be white, it must be recorded as blue. The reason for its blue color, when found, may be a valuable discovery.

QUESTIONS AND PROJECTS

1. Write a short report on a scientific discovery that interests you.

2. Find out how many tons of TNT are equivalent to
a. 1 pound of matter
b. 1 ounce of matter
c. 1 gram of matter

3. Visit a laboratory at your school or near your home and report on a particular project and how the investigator or investigators plan to obtain answers to a current problem.

4. Give from your own experience a personal example of how lack of objectivity produced or could have produced an incorrect conclusion.

5. Look up the name and structure of
a. A bactericide
b. A drug
c. A fungicide
d. A plastic

6. Find the names of 10 chemicals found in the human body.

7. Explain
a. Observations
b. Theory
c. Law

8. What does the chemist study and why?

9. Why is the law of conservation of mass not exact?

10. If you performed an experiment five times with identical results, and then performed it again with different results, what would be your reaction and what would you do next?

11. List the name and formula for 10 chemicals contained in products that are sold in a supermarket for use in the home.

12. Plan a simple chemical experiment. Discuss the various errors that could occur in carrying out this experiment.

13. Report on an interesting chemical research problem.

14. List three areas where you feel that chemical research should be initiated or improved.

15. Find out approximately how much electrical energy is consumed in an average city annually. Mass is converted into energy in a nuclear power plant. Determine how much mass will deliver the above quantity of power.

2

STRUCTURE OF THE ATOM

The research chemist is always asking the question "Why?" To set off a series of reactions and observe the results is useful, but if any real progress is to be made, the underlying reasons for reactions and properties must be discovered. Experimenters have for some time been trying to make an accurate picture of the atom so that we will have some basis for an explanation of observations and, more important, a basis for the prediction of future structures and properties.

LORD RUTHERFORD'S EXPERIMENT

An early experiment that produced a major "breakthrough" involved the use of very tiny positively charged particles, called alpha particles, emitted from a radioactive material. These particles were aimed at a thin metal foil. The location of the alpha particles could be detected by little flashes of light produced when the particles landed on a phosphorescent material placed behind or around the foil. The light flashes are just like the dots of light produced on your television screen. An interesting thing was observed. Most of the particles went straight through the foil, a few were deflected a little, and a very few bounded back. The explanation went as follows:

1. The atoms of metal foil, since they allowed almost all the particles to pass right through, must be mostly empty space.

2. Most of the mass of the atoms in the metal foil must be concentrated in a very small volume, since an occasional particle struck something and was bounced back.

3. This concentration of mass must be positively charged because the positively charged alpha particles that came close were repelled and hence deflected a little. (Recall that like charges repel and opposite charges attract.)

The picture of the atom soon became one in which most of the mass of the atom was concentrated in a nucleus. In this nucleus were particles called protons, having a positive charge, and neutrons, having no charge. Arranged around the nucleus at relatively large distances were negatively charged electrons equal in number to the positively charged protons, thus producing a neutral atom. For instance, the simplest atom contains one proton and one electron. Neutrons and protons, approximately equal in mass, are about 1,000 times heavier than electrons, which explains the large concentration of mass in the nucleus.

It is easy to talk about mass being concentrated in a very small volume, but we are actually talking about a world that is quite different from ours. For instance, think about a baseball made of only the cores of atoms—it would weigh ten thousand million tons! Think about the number of atoms in your body—you have approximately one billion billion billion atoms. As we continue our discussion, we should not be surprised if we find that we cannot translate all the rules that apply in our world to this strange and fascinating atomic world.

THE BOHR ATOM

To improve the picture of the atom, the chemist wanted next to know about the arrangement and stability of the electrons that somehow surround the nucleus. After all, if atoms are to react, they must come together, and since the electrons are on the outside, the reactions must involve the electrons. The physicist Niels Bohr pictured the electrons as traveling in various size circles about the nucleus. For the simplest atom, the hydrogen atom (which consists of only one proton and one electron), he wrote mathematical equations involving the positive-negative attractions between the proton and the electron and involving the speed of the electron in various circular orbits.

Now Bohr had to face ridicule in writing these equations because in them he contradicted some of the established laws of physics. In particular, he rejected a law stating that a charged body (the electron) moving about a charged nucleus (the proton) would gradually spiral into the nucleus while emitting radiation. Bohr based his rejection of this law on the fact that atoms do not collapse. The successful results of his calculations eventually quieted his critics.

Bohr's picture of the atom was substantiated as follows: His equations allowed him to calculate the energy of the electron in each of the circular orbits. Previous to Bohr's work, there had been many accurate observations of light that was emitted from heated hydrogen, the atom on which Bohr made his calculations. Certain distinct "lines of light" were detected and recorded for heated hydrogen, or as the spectroscopist calls it, "excited" hydrogen (Fig. 2–1).

I must at this point give a little description of light, more scientifically called electromagnetic radiation. Light comes in all sorts of frequencies, and each frequency has a corresponding wavelength. An easy way to understand frequency and wavelength is to imagine you are located on a warm and pleasant beach. The water, with its waves coming toward you in a periodic fashion, is exhibiting wave motion just as light exhibits wave motion. Counting the number of waves breaking per hour will give you the frequency rate. Now if you can estimate the distance between the crests of the waves, you will get what we call the wavelength.

Electromagnetic radiation has a pulsating electric field and a pulsating magnetic field and can come, as just stated, in various frequencies.

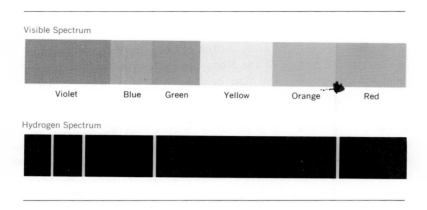

Visible Spectrum

Violet   Blue   Green   Yellow   Orange   Red

Hydrogen Spectrum

FIGURE 2–1

Further, a particular frequency will correspond to a particular energy. Let's go back to the beach to understand this. If the waves arrive at a high frequency, they can do quite a job of tearing up a beach or destroying a seawall, but if the waves arrive very infrequently, they do not represent as much energy. You can think of light in the same way. Light of high frequency is high in energy; light of low frequency is low in energy. It is time to roll up the beach blanket and come back to the atom. The various lines of light that were observed being emitted from heated hydrogen corresponded to very definite frequencies and, hence, to definite energies. In the Bohr hydrogen atom, one can visualize the lone electron, on being heated, jumping up to an orbit farther away from the nucleus. Eventually the electron will return to its original orbit. If we now liken these orbits to shelves in a bookcase and imagine the electron as a book, we know that it takes energy to lift a book, say, from the bottom shelf to a higher shelf. If the book fell back to the bottom shelf, the energy we invested would be returned. The shelf would be jarred by the blow, dust might fly, and certainly noise would be heard.

What about the excited electron when it returns to its original orbit—how do we get our energy back? Perhaps in the form of lines of light! Indeed, when Bohr calculated the differences in energies between the various orbits, these energy differences corresponded precisely to the frequencies of the lines of light. Bohr's basic assumptions, then, must have been correct, since the results of his equations compared exactly with independent sets of data. However, Bohr's theory, as triumphant as it was, could not explain the spectral data from more complicated atoms, and it remained for others to apply some new approaches to get a more precise picture of the atom.

WAVE NATURE OF MATTER

A scientist named De Broglie conceived the following explanation: Since light can have a frequency corresponding to a particular energy, and since light can emerge as a result of changes in matter (electrons returning to lower levels), then perhaps matter itself with a particular energy of motion will exhibit a corresponding frequency. De Broglie's assumption was demonstrated and shown to be accurate. It may be a little difficult for us to believe that we are all involved in "wave motion," but again the atomic world is a strange one. Since matter was shown to have wave motion, the equations of waves were included in the hydrogen atom system.

The solution of these rather complicated equations gave us a more complete, but somewhat more involved, picture of the hydrogen atom. Instead of the simple, circular Bohr orbits, also referred to as shells, we find that there are major shells, there are subshells within the major shells, and within these subshells there are variously shaped volumes of space called orbitals. We find that each orbital may house one or two electrons.

Contrary to Bohr's pinpointing the location of the speeding electron, it became clear that we could not know the exact location and speed of the electron at the same time. However, we can predict where the electron spends, say, 95 percent of its time. The amount of time the electron spends in various locations is called "probability density." The best way to picture this is to consider the hydrogen atom with the electron in its most stable orbital. If we make ourselves as small as an electron and start walking toward the hydrogen nucleus, we can *imagine* there is a ball-shaped cloud around the nucleus (see Fig. 2–2). Where the cloud is thin, we know the electron spends not too much time, but

FIGURE 2–2   s ORBITAL.

where the cloud is thick, the electron spends a lot of time. We enter the cloud and find that it is thin on the fringes and thick near the center. Other orbitals have different shapes, but the idea is the same. This is our new concept of the atom, considerably different from the simpler Bohr picture.

The wave-motion theory, although it gives us a "foggier" picture of the atom, does give us a more exact and useful one. It explains much more of the observed data than Bohr's simpler theory could ever do. In the next chapter, we shall see how, according to this modern theory, the electrons and protons are arranged in the elements that we know today.

QUESTIONS AND PROJECTS

1. Describe Rutherford's experiment.

2. What insight into the structure of the atom was gained from Rutherford's experiment?

3. Why are alpha particles repelled by nuclei?

4. Compare charge and mass of the electron and the proton.

5. Assume an average weight for a man and for a mouse. Approximately how many atoms are there in the mouse?

6. Assume that a dime could be constructed out of cores of atoms. What would the dime weigh?

7. Explain how lines of light are emitted from excited hydrogen gas.

8. For electromagnetic radiation what is
a. The frequency?
b. The wavelength?
c. The relation between energy and frequency?

9. Compare the Bohr picture and the modern picture of the atom.

10. What is meant by
a. Major shells?
b. Subshells?
c. Orbitals?
d. Probability density?

11. Look up the equation that Bohr wrote to describe the energy levels in the hydrogen atom.

12. The equation that described the "lines of light" was known before Bohr developed his equation. Look up this equation, which is called the Rydberg equation. Comment on the similarity between this equation and Bohr's.

13. Assume that five waves strike a particular beach every minute and that the distance between the wave crests is exactly 30 feet. Calculate the speed of the wave. What is its frequency? What is the wavelength? Draw a diagram indicating the wavelength.

14. Given two atoms as follows:
Atom A: five neutrons, five protons and five electrons.
Atom B: four neutrons, six protons and six electrons.
a. Which atom has the larger mass?
b. Which nucleus is heavier?
c. Which nucleus has the greater electrostatic charge?

15. When certain metallic salts are heated in a flame, a pronounced color is observed. Sodium salts give a yellowish flame, bariums give green calciums give red, etc. What do you think is the origin of the colors?

3

THE
ELEMENTS
AND THEIR
FAMILIES

So far we have discussed only the simplest atom of all the 104 elements that we know today. The hydrogen atom contains one proton and one electron. We recall that a nucleus can contain uncharged particles called neutrons. These neutrons alter the mass of an element but generally do not change the chemical nature of the element. For example, some hydrogen atoms have a neutron in addition to a proton in the nucleus. Since the neutron and proton have about the same mass and since the electron's mass is very small compared to either the neutron's or the proton's, the mass of the atom is essentially doubled. This special

◀ PHOTO COURTESY OF PAUL SELIGMAN.

hydrogen atom is called heavy hydrogen, or deuterium. However, the atom still exhibits chemical properties typical of the element hydrogen.

PERIODIC ARRANGEMENT OF ELEMENTS

The number of protons in the nucleus determines what the element is. We call this number the atomic number. In Fig. 3–1, a *periodic chart* of the elements (so called because the elements are arranged in a special periodic pattern), the atomic numbers of the elements are indicated in gold. The elements are also indicated by their chemical symbols. For instance, H stands for hydrogen, He for helium, S for sulfur, Cl for chlorine, and Na for sodium. The arrangement of the elements will become clear to you as we consider the arrangement of the electrons in one element after another.

The wave-motion equations tell us there are shells, subshells, and orbitals, with each orbital capable of housing a total of two electrons.

I												III	IV	V	VI	VII	VIII
1 H $1s^1$	II															1 H $1s^1$	2 He $1s^2$
3 Li $2s^1$	4 Be $2s^2$											5 B $2p^1$	6 C $2p^2$	7 N $2p^3$	8 O $2p^4$	9 F $2p^5$	10 Ne $2p^6$
11 Na $3s^1$	12 Mg $3s^2$											13 Al $3p^1$	14 Si $3p^2$	15 P $3p^3$	16 S $3p^4$	17 Cl $3p^5$	18 Ar $3p^6$
19 K $4s^1$	20 Ca $4s^2$	21 Sc $3d$	22 Ti	23 V	24 Cr	25 Mn	26 Fe	27 Co	28 Ni	29 Cu	30 Zn →	31 Ga $4p^1$	32 Ge $4p^2$	33 As $4p^3$	34 Se $4p^4$	35 Br $4p^5$	36 Kr $4p^6$
37 Rb $5s^1$	38 Sr $5s^2$	39 Y $4d$	40 Zr	41 Nb	42 Mo	43 Tc	44 Ru	45 Rh	46 Pd	47 Ag	48 Cd →	49 In $5p^1$	50 Sn $5p^2$	51 Sb $5p^3$	52 Te $5p^4$	53 I $5p^5$	54 Xe $5p^6$
55 Cs $6s^1$	56 Ba $6s^2$	57 La $5d$	72 Hf	73 Ta	74 W	75 Re	76 Os	77 Ir	78 Pt	79 Au	80 Hg →	81 Tl $6p^1$	82 Pb $6p^2$	83 Bi $6p^3$	84 Po $6p^4$	85 At $6p^5$	86 Rn $6p^6$
87 Fr $7s^1$	88 Ra $7s^2$	89 Ac $6d^1$	104														

58 Ce $4f$	59 Pr	60 Nd	61 Pm	62 Sm	63 Eu	64 Gd	65 Tb	66 Dy	67 Ho	68 Er	69 Tm	70 Yb	71 Lu →
90 Th $5f$	91 Pa	92 U	93 Np	94 Pu	95 Am	96 Cm	97 Bk	98 Cf	99 Es	100 Fm	101 Md	102 No	103 Lr →

FIGURE 3–1   PERIODIC CHART OF THE ELEMENTS.

The shells are numbered 1, 2, 3, etc., with the lowest numbers closest to the nucleus and therefore of the lowest energy, just as in a bookcase, the books on the lowest shelves would have the least energy, and the books on the highest shelves would have the most. The shells with the higher numbers are farther out from the nucleus and are therefore larger shells. Larger shells can, of course, accommodate more subshells. Let's go back to hydrogen with its lone electron. The electron normally spends its time in the first shell. The first shell, being small, has only one subshell called the 1s subshell. An s subshell has only one orbital called the s orbital (s subshell and s orbital therefore mean the same thing). We saw in Fig. 2–2 that this orbital was ball-shaped or spherical. All s orbitals, whether in the first shell or a higher shell, are spherical. Notice that the s orbital for the uncombined hydrogen atom has only one electron, although it was stated that any orbital can hold one or two electrons.

Consider now the second major shell. This is larger than the first and has two subshells, an s subshell called 2s and a p subshell called 2p. All p orbitals are approximately dumbbell-shaped (see Fig. 3–2). The 2s subshell, like the 1s, has only one orbital, called the 2s orbital, but the 2p subshell has three orbitals, each again capable of housing two electrons. Therefore, in the second shell there is room for two electrons in the 2s orbital and six electrons in the three 2p orbitals.

The third shell, being still larger, can have three subshells, s, p, and d, with the d having five orbitals. The fourth shell can have four subshells, s, p, d, and f, with the f having seven orbitals, and so forth. Figure 3–3 summarizes what is presented above.

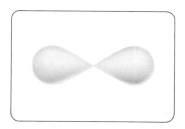

FIGURE 3–2   p ORBITAL.

SHELL	SUBSHELLS	ORBITALS	TOTAL NO. OF ELECTRONS
1	s	1 s	2
2	s, p	1 s, 3 p's	8
3	s, p, d	1 s, 3 p's	
		5 d's	18
4	s, p, d, f	1 s, 3 p's	
		5 d's, 7 f's	32

FIGURE 3–3

This will become clearer if we gradually consider one element after another and see where each electron is. Assume that we have great powers that allow us to create atoms and to change them from one atom to another simply by adding or subtracting protons and electrons. Since the neutrons do not change the chemical nature of the elements, we will omit them from our discussion.

BUILDUP OF ATOMS

In the hydrogen atom, the sole electron is located in the 1s orbital. We record this with the notation $1s^1$, which means there is one electron (superscript ^{1}) in the s subshell of the first major shell. The next larger element, helium, will have two protons and, of course, two electrons. Since the s orbital can hold two electrons, the next electron will go into this orbital, and the notation will become $1s^2$, meaning there are two electrons in the s orbital of the first shell. (Refer to Fig. 3–1.)

You may quickly say, "Why should the two electrons, which are both negatively charged and hence repel one another, occupy the same orbital? Why does not the second electron occupy a position in, say, the second major shell?" We have to go back to the bookcase comparison for an explanation. To be accurate I will have to readjust the shelves to represent the energy levels in the atom. Near the bottom, I place the shelves far apart, but toward the ceiling I place them closer and closer together until some nearly overlap. This is the situation in the atom; that second electron had a choice of going way up to the second shell or forcing itself to overcome the repulsion of the first electron and share its 1s orbital. It happens that the latter is much easier to do, and that is why the arrangement for the element helium, atomic number 2 (two protons), becomes $1s^2$.

SECOND PERIOD

Now for the next element. Let's add a proton to the helium nucleus and find a spot for the third electron. I continue to build upward, just as I might fill the bookcase from the bottom up. Since the first shell is now completely filled, I must go to the second. The s subshell always fills first, so that the electron goes into the 2s orbital, and the notation for this element, lithium, atomic number 3, becomes $1s^2 2s^1$. This says that there is one electron in the s orbital of the second shell and there are two electrons in the s orbital of the first shell. There is room for another electron in the 2s so that the next element will house its fourth electron in the 2s orbital (notation $1s^2 2s^2$ for atomic number 4, beryllium).

The next element must utilize one of the three 2p orbitals. It doesn't matter which of the three the electron enters, since all three are of equal energy. The following electron will have a choice of going into the same 2p orbital as the last electron did or into an empty 2p orbital. Since you know that electrons are negatively charged and do repel one another, you will correctly conclude that the next electron will prefer to go into an empty 2p orbital. This continues until, with atomic number 7, nitrogen, all three 2p orbitals have one electron each.

With oxygen, there is a choice of joining up with an electron in one of the 2p orbitals or of going way up to the third major shell. As you might guess, it is easier for the electron to enter a 2p orbital. The notation for oxygen, atomic number 8, then becomes $1s^2 2s^2 2p^4$. Atomic number 9, fluorine, becomes $1s^2 2s^2 2p^5$, and neon, atomic number 10, becomes $1s^2 2s^2 2p^6$. Note that with neon the s and p subshells are completely filled and thus the second shell is completely filled. Chemists have observed that structures with completed subshells and completed shells are relatively inactive or stable structures.

THIRD PERIOD

Please keep referring back to Fig. 3–1 as we continue to "create" atoms by adding another proton and electron to neon, atomic number 10. This electron imitates the last sequence or "period," which started with lithium. The electron goes into the 3s orbital. Magnesium becomes $3s^2$, aluminum $3p^1$, silicon $3p^2$, etc., up to argon which has the configuration $1s^2 2s^2 2p^6 3s^2 3p^6$. Argon, like neon, has completed s and p subshells. The third shell, however, being larger than the second, also has a d subshell called 3d, with a total of five orbitals. Therefore, argon completes its period, the third period, but does not have a completed third shell.

FOURTH AND FIFTH PERIODS

You recall that the higher levels of the atoms, like the levels of the special bookcase, got closer and closer together as they got farther from the nucleus. In fact, some of the levels get so close that they even overlap. This occurs in the fourth period, which, you can see in Fig. 3–1, is a long one. Atomic numbers 19 and 20, potassium and calcium, have their electrons in the 4s orbital, which at this point is lower in energy than the d subshell of the third shell (3d). After the 4s orbital is occupied, the 3d subshell commences to be filled. Its five orbitals, with two electrons each, account for a total of 10 electrons and therefore for 10 elements, atomic numbers 21 through 30, scandium through zinc.

Having finished filling the 3d level, we continue in a normal fashion with the 4p (atomic numbers 31 to 36). In the fifth period, the same sort of overlapping occurs again; the 5s fills first, then the 4d, then back to the 5p.

SIXTH AND SEVENTH PERIODS

In the sixth period, a double overlapping occurs. Recall that the fourth shell has an s, p, d, and f subshell. We have not yet completed the fourth shell. What happens is this: The 6s is filled; one electron enters the 5d level, atomic number 57, lanthanum. The 4f level is then filled, atomic numbers 58 to 71, and then we go back to finish the 5d level, atomic numbers 72 to 80. After that, we return as before to a p level, the 6p, which is then filled with atomic number 86. You can see in Fig. 3–1 that the same irregularities repeat in the filling of the 5f, atomic numbers 90 through 103.

You may have to go back over the last paragraphs to digest what has been presented, but if you study Fig. 3–3, which summarizes the orbitals, I am sure you will have no trouble. The order of filling is as follows: $1s$, $2s$, $2p$, $3s$, $3p$, $4s$, $3d$, $4p$, $5s$, $4d$, $5p$, $6s$, $5d^1$, $4f^{14}$, $5d^9$, $6p^6$, $7s^2$, $6d^1$, $5f^{14}$.

CHEMICAL FAMILIES

Please note that columns of elements have similar electron arrangements. For instance, in Column I all the elements have one electron in an unfilled s level, with all the previous s and p levels filled. Column II has two electrons, with all the previous s and p levels filled. Column VIII has its last s and p levels completely filled; Column VII is one short of having its last s and p levels filled; and Column VI is two short of having its last s and p levels filled. Indeed, the elements within each column have very distinct chemical similarities. The reactions they undergo, the structures they form, and the properties they exhibit are so similar that we call them families. Column I is the alkali family, Column II is the alkaline earth family, Column VI is the oxygen family, Column VII is the halogen family, and Column VIII is the inert gas family.

This arrangement of atoms which we have built based upon the results of the wave-motion equations, this periodic chart, was actually developed long before the wave equations were ever applied to the hydrogen atom. Chemists, who diligently experimented, observed, and recorded data on the various elements, were alert to the fact that there were many similarities in properties. They prepared charts based upon the known elements and used them to make remarkable predictions about the properties of elements yet undiscovered. The fact that the chart based upon the wave-motion equations checks closely with the chart based upon numerous other experimental data gives ample justification to the

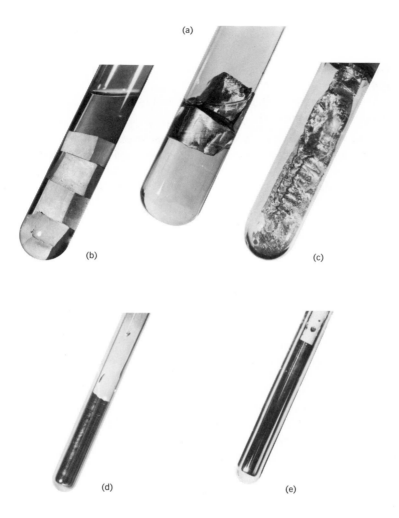

FIGURE 3–4   FAMILY PORTRAIT OF THE METALS IN COLUMN I OF THE PERIODIC
TABLE: (a) LITHIUM, (b) SODIUM, (c) POTASSIUM, (d) RUBIDIUM,
AND (e) CESIUM. NOTICE THE SIMILARITY IN APPEARANCE. WHY
ARE THE TUBES FILLED WITH KEROSENE OR SEALED OFF FROM
THE AIR? (COURTESY OF B. M. SHAUB.)

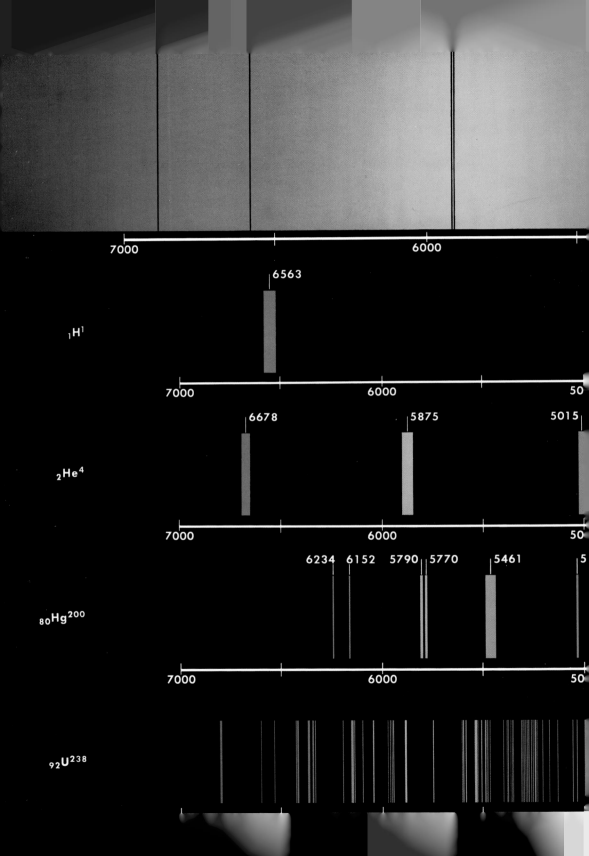

7000   6000

6563

₁H¹

7000   6000   50

6678   5875   5015

₂He⁴

7000   6000   50

6234   6152   5790 5770   5461   5

₈₀Hg²⁰⁰

7000   6000   50

₉₂U²³⁸

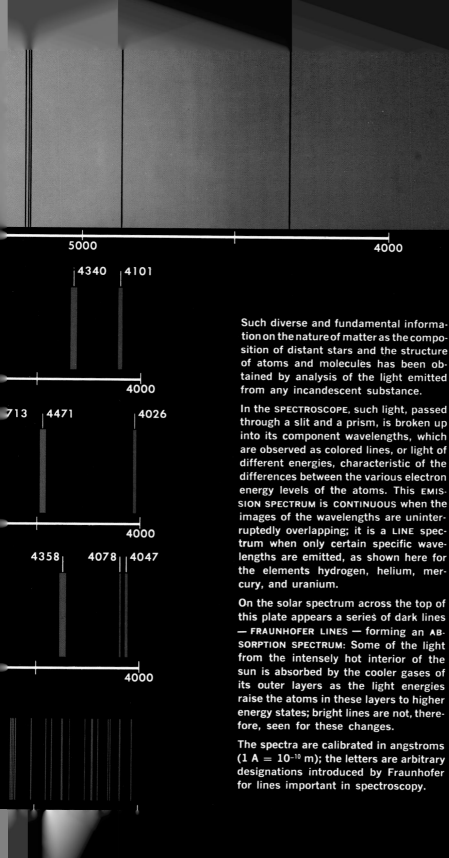

Such diverse and fundamental information on the nature of matter as the composition of distant stars and the structure of atoms and molecules has been obtained by analysis of the light emitted from any incandescent substance.

In the SPECTROSCOPE, such light, passed through a slit and a prism, is broken up into its component wavelengths, which are observed as colored lines, or light of different energies, characteristic of the differences between the various electron energy levels of the atoms. This EMISSION SPECTRUM is CONTINUOUS when the images of the wavelengths are uninterruptedly overlapping; it is a LINE spectrum when only certain specific wavelengths are emitted, as shown here for the elements hydrogen, helium, mercury, and uranium.

On the solar spectrum across the top of this plate appears a series of dark lines — FRAUNHOFER LINES — forming an ABSORPTION SPECTRUM: Some of the light from the intensely hot interior of the sun is absorbed by the cooler gases of its outer layers as the light energies raise the atoms in these layers to higher energy states; bright lines are not, therefore, seen for these changes.

The spectra are calibrated in angstroms ($1 A = 10^{-10}$ m); the letters are arbitrary designations introduced by Fraunhofer for lines important in spectroscopy.

assumptions used in developing our modern atomic theory. The ultimate test of that theory is its ability to predict such things as what kind of unions are possible between atoms, how strong these unions may be, and what properties are associated with them.

Let me say that so far I have been insisting that there are always the same number of electrons as protons. This is true for the undisturbed, unreacted atoms, but the situation can be changed. Some elements tend to gain electrons, some tend to lose electrons, and some prefer to share electrons with other atoms. In the next chapter, we will see how electronic arrangements undergo changes as the atoms interact with one another.

QUESTIONS AND PROJECTS

1. What is the shape of
a. An s orbital?
b. A p orbital?

2. In a given major shell, which subshell fills first?

3. How many electrons can occupy
a. One orbital?
b. An s subshell?
c. A p subshell?
d. A d subshell?
e. An f subshell?

4. How many electrons can occupy
a. The first major shell?
b. The second major shell?
c. The third major shell?
d. Half a d subshell?
e. Seven f orbitals?

5. What is
a. Atomic number?
b. Deuterium?
c. The nucleus of the hydrogen atom?
d. The mass of deuterium compared to the mass of hydrogen?

6. Describe the relative positions of the energy levels in an atom.

7. Why does the 1s subshell fill before starting on the 2s?

8. What amount of filling of a subshell corresponds to stability?

9. How was the periodic chart developed before modern atomic theory?

10. Give the electronic notations for the following atoms:

a. Helium   f. Titanium
b. Carbon   g. Lead
c. Silicon   h. Bromine
d. Chlorine   i. Potassium
e. Argon   j. Samarium

11. In the phosphorus atom how many electrons are in s orbitals? How many in p? How many more electrons would be needed to fill the 3p subshell? If this happened, the phosphorus atom would then have an electronic arrangement identical with what inert gas?

12. Write out the order of filling of electrons in the various levels.

13. The ground state for chromium is ....$3d^54s^1$ and the ground state for copper is ......$3d^{10}4s^1$. Keeping in mind that the 4s and 3d levels are not much different in energy, explain the above configurations.

14. What is the name of the element for which

a. The nucleus contains 7 protons and 7 neutrons?
b. The nucleus contains 7 protons and 8 neutrons?
c. The nucleus contains 11 protons and 11 neutrons?
d. The nucleus contains 11 protons and 12 neutrons?

15. Name as many chemical families as you can and indicate their location on the periodic chart.

4

CHEMICAL BONDING

In studying the individual atom and the electronic structure of the various elements, our goal was to be able to use our fundamental knowledge to explain observations and, more important, to predict future reactions, structures, and properties. We will now consider how atoms can come together and stay together in various arrangements. Atoms must come close to one another to form a bond, and as stated before, since the outside of the atom is a blanket of electrons, it is evident that somehow the electrons must be involved in bonding.

To begin to understand the basis for bond formation, we observe reactive and unreactive elements and their respective electronic structures. For instance, the elements in Column VIII, starting with He, helium, are all gases and are all relatively inert, compared to the other elements. They are not quite so completely inert as we used to think they were, but still by comparison they are very unreactive, and consequently, we consider their structures to be "stable" structures. It would now be logical to assume that if other elements could somehow alter their electronic arrangements so that they were like the inert gas structures, they too would become stable or unreactive. Indeed, other elements enter into such reactions as lead to these stable inert gas structures. A useful comparison is to think of a valley with a boulder in the bottom as representing the inert gas structure. Now think of a valley with a boulder teetering on the hill above; this represents an element waiting for a shove, waiting for a reaction to take place, after which it will attain the stable structure.

IONIC BONDING

Helium has two electrons in the s subshell of the first shell, and hence its first shell is completely filled. The inert gases, neon to radon, all have the s and p orbitals of their outermost shell completely filled. Completed shell and completed subshell configurations are stable ones, and elements, through reactions, tend toward stable configurations.

As our first example, let's take a substance with which we are all familiar—table salt, called sodium chloride by chemists. As you can guess, this compound comes from the two elements sodium, atomic number 11, and chlorine, atomic number 17. Sodium's electronic configuration, $1s^22s^22p^63s^1$, is exactly the same as neon's configuration, except that it has one more electron. We also know that sodium has one more proton in its nucleus than neon has, but remember we are only talking about the arrangement of the blanket of electrons. Chlorine has the configuration $1s^22s^22p^63s^23p^5$; its arrangement would be the same as argon, atomic number 18, if it had one more electron. You can see what can happen: sodium will lose its extra electron, and chlorine will gladly accept it. Two boulders have rolled down to the bottom of the valley.

Notice that sodium now has one more proton than electrons, and chlorine has one more electron than protons. Sodium has a positive charge, and chlorine has a negative charge. These charged particles are called ions; they are named the sodium ion, a cation, and the chloride ion, an anion. The resulting compound is tasty table salt, sodium chloride. If you have ever played with a pair of magnets, you know how the opposite poles attract one another, and you remember that it is hard to get the magnets apart when they are very close together. The ions with their opposite charges are likewise attracted to one another. This is a very strong factor for this reaction between sodium and chlorine to take place and for the resulting product, sodium chloride, which is written, in our shorthand method, NaCl, to be stable.

Previously we got a feeling for the minute size of an atom, so that when we speak of a teaspoonful of salt we are not surprised to know that we are talking about billions of atoms. When a small amount of sodium and chlorine react, then, we are dealing with billions of little positive ions and billions of little negative ions. It is fairly accurate to consider the ions to be charged particles shaped like balls, with opposite charges attracting and like charges repelling. Think of a jar of red marbles and a jar of green marbles. Giving you a powerful glue, I tell you to stick all the marbles together in a regular and symmetrical pattern. You can imagine the kind of structure you would obtain. The sodium and chloride ions fall into such an arrangement, with six chloride ions surrounding each sodium ion and six sodium ions surrounding each chloride ion (see Fig. 4–1). This arrangement, called a crystal or lattice, repeats itself in every direction. Ionic compounds will have lattices similar to those of the sodium-chloride structure. The exact pattern will depend upon the charges and relative sizes of the ions.

What we have just described is a very important type of chemical bonding called ionic bonding. Let us look at one more example of an ionic

FIGURE 4–1   SODIUM CHLORIDE
CRYSTAL.

compound before going on to another type of bonding. Calcium chloride is a compound that has the property of absorbing water. It does so better than table salt, which, we have all observed, becomes caked in hot, humid weather. Calcium chloride is used on highways to melt ice, in the

FIGURE 4—1a   THE BRICK-LIKE SHAPE OF THESE NATURAL CRYSTALS RE-
FLECTS THE FORM OF THE IONIC LATTICE. (*COURTESY OF
B. M. SHAUB.*)

laboratories to keep other chemicals dry, and in concrete to prevent freezing in cold weather.

The structure of calcium, atomic number 20, has just two more electrons than the stable structure of argon, atomic number 18. Chlorine, again, has one less electron than argon. Calcium has two electrons to get rid of, and since each chlorine atom can only accept one electron, it will take two chlorine atoms to satisfy each calcium atom. Notice that calcium will have two more protons than electrons and hence a double positive charge, while each chlorine atom, with one more electron than proton, will have a single negative charge. The positive calcium ions attract the negative chloride ions. They form a crystalline lattice, and the resulting stable ionic compound is called calcium chloride, written $CaCl_2$. The subscript 2 says that there are two chloride ions for every calcium ion.

Keep in mind that in an ionic compound the type of union is only a positive-negative charge attraction. It is like the two magnets held close together with a strong attractive force but with nothing in between. The next kind of union that we will consider will be more deserving of the expression "bond."

COVALENT BONDING

The uncombined hydrogen atom has only one electron in its first shell, although the first shell can hold two electrons as it does in helium, a stable element. Therefore, we would not be surprised to see hydrogen try to gain the helium structure, the completed first shell. Eavesdropping on a conversation between two hydrogen atoms, we might hear from the first hydrogen atom, "How about giving me your electron so that I can have a lovely completed shell?" The reply comes back, "Oh, no. A far better arrangement would be for you to give me your electron. I, too, want a completed shell." And since neither identical hydrogen atom is more powerful or more persuasive than the other, there develops an impasse. Finally, they come up with the idea of sharing the two electrons, that is, of bringing both atoms close together and letting the electrons spend time in both 1s orbitals (Fig. 4–2). This is not as good as each atom having two electrons, but it is the best arrangement possible. This is the situation that we observe; the hydrogen atoms run around in

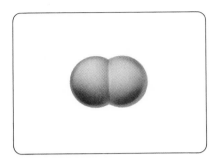

FIGURE 4–2   **HYDROGEN MOLECULE.**

pairs called hydrogen *molecules,* written H_2. This type of bonding is called *covalent.* In ionic bonding, there are no molecules, only large numbers of ions held together by positive-negative attractions.

VALENCE-BOND AND MOLECULAR ORBITAL THEORIES

When the two hydrogen atoms approached one another, each had one electron in a 1s ball-shaped orbital. Remember that the nuclei of atoms are positively charged and therefore will repel each other if brought very close together. As the atoms come near each other, we can picture the ball-shaped orbitals intersecting one another so that there is a very dense fog between the atoms. In effect, both electrons are now spending a lot of time between the two atoms, and since electrons are negatively charged, they are neutralizing the positive-positive repulsion between the two hydrogen nuclei. This picture of covalent bonding is called the *valence-bond theory.*

Another modern approach is to consider that, after formation of the molecules from the atoms, we no longer have atomic orbitals. Rather, all the electrons really belong to the molecule, and therefore we have a brand new set of orbitals called *molecular orbitals.* This approach, although rather more complicated, explains some situations that are difficult or impossible to explain with the valence-bond theory. On the other hand, the valence-bond theory, since it is much easier to visualize and since it is accurate in most cases, is still the theory most commonly used.

In Chap. 2, we pointed out how the law of conservation of mass had to be adjusted and how Bohr's theory was replaced by another. It is the nature of chemistry, as an experimental science, to have its theories continually reevaluated and to have them replaced in the light of new data or new calculations. It is not important that you know the status of each current chemical theory, but it is important that you be aware that chemists are steadfastly studying, observing, adding to their reservoir of knowledge, and improving their theories and laws. The author's feeling is that, although science has made many fascinating advances, we have really only scratched the surface of knowledge. It remains for this generation and future generations to build on existing data and make many more discoveries. In particular, there will probably develop new and superior theories of structure and bonding which will replace our present concepts and provide greater insight and predictability.

Let us look at more examples of covalent bonding. Hydrogen chloride, when dissolved in water, is an acid called hydrochloric or muriatic acid, which has many uses. In the building industry, for instance, it is used to clean newly installed tile or brickwork. The isolated hydrogen atom has its one electron in the 1s orbital. Chlorine, if you look back at Fig. 3–1, has five p electrons in its 3p subshell. With one more electron, it would have completed s and p subshells, just like argon. There are in a p subshell three p orbitals, which we pointed out were shaped like dumbbells.

Fig. 4–3 shows a pair of p orbitals at right angles to each other. The third p orbital is at right angles to both of these. In other words, the third orbital comes up out of the page and goes down behind the page. In any p subshell the orbitals have this arrangement.

Now the chlorine atom, before reaction, has five electrons in the 3p subshell. This means, then, that two of the 3p orbitals are filled with two electrons each, and the third p orbital has only one electron and is waiting for another. You can see in Fig. 4–4 how the hydrogen atom can overlap its 1s orbital with the half-filled 3p orbital of the chlorine atom. (The filled p orbitals are the dark ones.) Now the 1s electron of hydrogen is spending time in its own orbital as well as in the 3p orbital of chlorine. The solitary 3p electron of chlorine is now spending time in

FIGURE 4–3   TWO p ORBITALS.

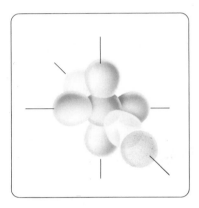

FIGURE 4–4   HYDROGEN ATOM AND
CHLORINE ATOM.

its own orbital as well as time in the 1s hydrogen orbital. Both electrons spend a lot of time (high-probability density) in between the two atoms, again reducing the positive-positive repulsion of the two nuclei.

We have just witnessed the formation of a covalent bond by the overlapping of s and p orbitals. For the hydrogen molecule, there was overlapping of two s orbitals. You can now visualize how the chlorine molecule Cl_2 can be produced by the overlapping of the two half-filled p orbitals. Almost all orbitals can overlap to produce covalent bonding. In fact, there can be overlapping of more than one pair of orbitals to produce double bonding (two pairs of electrons involved) or triple bonding (three pairs of electrons involved). Overlapping of just one pair of orbitals to form a covalent bond is called *single covalent bonding*.

HYBRID ORBITALS

So far, our discussion of covalent bonding has been limited to pairs of atoms, which join to form molecules that we call diatomic. We are, of course, interested in the shapes of molecules, for the way molecules might "fit" together is important in predicting reactions and properties. There is no problem with two atoms; they must lie in a straight line. However, with three or more atoms, there are a variety of possibilities. To explain some of the observed shapes of molecules, we assume that some of the individual atomic orbitals of a particular atom are capable of interacting with each other and forming new orbitals, which we accordingly call *hybrid orbitals*. For instance, an s and a p orbital in the same atom can combine to form two sp orbitals (see Fig. 4–5) arranged in a straight line; an s and two p's can form three sp^2 orbitals which

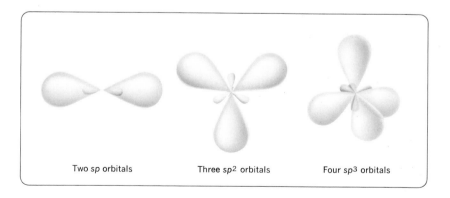

Two sp orbitals   Three sp^2 orbitals   Four sp^3 orbitals

FIGURE 4–5   **HYBRID ORBITALS.**

point to the corners of an equilateral triangle; and an s and three p orbitals can form four sp^3 orbitals which point to the four corners of an equal-sided triangular pyramid. Such combinations of orbitals yield hybrid orbitals which account for other observed molecular arrangements.

When the chemist wishes to represent a particular structure, he cannot always take the time to draw diagrams of the orbitals. He must have a shorthand method of representation. For instance, an ionic compound is written as NaCl or $CaCl_2$, etc. A covalent compound is written similarly as H_2, Cl_2, or HCl. However, it is important to show covalent bonds in more detail, and you will commonly see formulas such as these: hydrogen, H—H; chlorine, Cl—Cl; hydrogen chloride, H—Cl; ethylene, $\begin{smallmatrix} H \\ H \end{smallmatrix}>C=C<\begin{smallmatrix} H \\ H' \end{smallmatrix}$; or acetylene, H—C≡C—H. The single line represents an overlapping of a pair of orbitals with two electrons being involved, that is, a single covalent bond. The double lines represent the overlapping of two pairs of orbitals with four electrons involved or a double covalent bond. The triple lines represent the overlapping of three pairs of orbitals with six electrons being involved, or a triple covalent bond.

Before entering the applied areas of chemistry, it will be very profitable for you to have a more complete understanding of the naming system used by chemists, the rules for writing formulas of compounds, and the methods for writing equations which represent chemical reactions. The following chapter will give an introduction of these topics.

QUESTIONS AND PROJECTS

1. Give the electronic notation for

a. Magnesium ion
b. Potassium ion
c. Fluoride ion
d. Sulfide ion
e. Neon
f. Argon
g. Strontium ion
h. Krypton

2. With plastic foam balls build a sodium chloride lattice.

3. Explain why ionic compounds form.

4. Find out how many ions are in 1 pound of salt.

5. Compare ionic and covalent bonding.

6. Describe roughly the probability density of the hydrogen molecule. Explain the resultant stability.

7. Make foam ball models for
a. Hydrogen molecule
b. Hydrogen chloride molecule
c. Chlorine molecule

8. Describe and give examples for
a. Single covalent bond
b. Double covalent bond
c. Triple covalent bond

9. Give names of compounds which exhibit the following types of hybrid bonding:
a. sp
b. sp^2
c. sp^3

10. Make foam ball models of the above examples of hybrid bonding.

11. The H_2S molecule exists in a shape that is close to a right angle. Predict what orbitals are involved in the bonding. Make a foam ball model of H_2S.

12. Elements of Columns I and II commonly join with elements of Columns VI and VII to form ionic compounds. Give the names and formulas of five ionic compounds.

13. State whether there are any repulsions possible in the sodium chloride lattice. If so, why is the lattice stable?

14. The type of overlapping of orbitals discussed so far is called sigma bonding. Here the overlapping takes place along the axis between the two atoms. If two p orbitals (one from each atom) are parallel to one another and are not far apart they can overlap sideways. This is called pi bonding. Make a foam ball model of two atoms exhibiting (a) sigma bonding alone and (b) sigma bonding and pi bonding.

15. Ethylene, $\begin{smallmatrix} H \\ H \end{smallmatrix}>C{=}C<\begin{smallmatrix} H \\ H \end{smallmatrix}$, exhibits sigma and pi bonding simultaneously. Each carbon atom has sp^2 hybrid bonding and a p orbital at right angles to the hybrid bonds. The p orbitals overlap sideways. Make a foam ball model of ethylene.

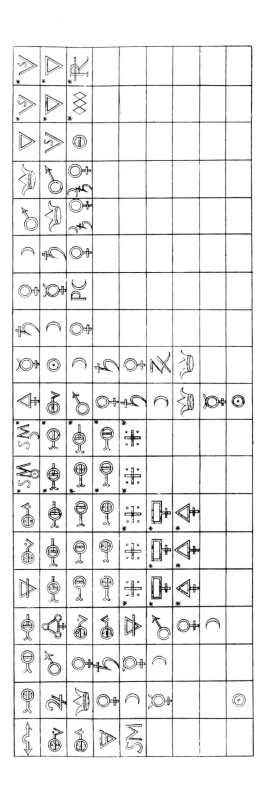

5

NAMES, FORMULAS, AND EQUATIONS

In the previous chapters we have used some chemical names, most of them familiar to you, and have written a few basic formulas. In order to discuss a number of modern topics which involve chemistry we will have to face other names and formulas considerably more complex. These frightening names and strange-looking formulas are probably responsible for most people's avoidance of the subject of chemistry. Actually, understanding these names and formulas is not a difficult feat at all. One could draw a comparison with the study of the Russian language by an American student. The Russian letters are at first sight so confusing that the student may feel that the language is impossible to master. Persons who have studied Russian will tell you this is not true.

It is the object, then, of this chapter to show that the language of chemistry is actually rather simple. When you have learned the basic facts involved, you will have more of an appreciation for a name, a formula, or an equation when you run into it in the future.

We will start with the symbols for the elements themselves. You may refer to the periodic chart in Fig. 3–1, where they are all listed. Why do we use these funny single and double letters at all? Well, it would be very cumbersome to write out the complete name for each element; when you consider that some compounds contain many different elements, you realize that the names for the compounds would be quite long indeed. Therefore, as in many other fields, a shorthand method has been adopted. Since we have 104 elements and only 26 letters in our alphabet, it is difficult to avoid overlapping of symbols. Therefore, some of the symbols are derived directly from the English names while others come from the Latin, Greek, French, or German names for the elements. For instance, S stands for sulfur and Na (from the Latin *natrium*) for sodium. It is interesting to note that of all the elements present on earth, 13 make up 98 percent of the crust of the earth, including the oceans and the air. (See Fig. 5–1.) Many of the elements exist only in small amounts.

However, the fact that an element is present on earth in small quantities does not necessarily mean that it is unimportant. We know, for instance, that lack of small amounts of certain minerals in our diet can bring about serious disorders. In Fig. 5–2 is a list of elements that will

---

THE THIRTEEN MOST COMMON ELEMENTS, WHICH MAKE UP 98% OF THE EARTH'S CRUST

1. Oxygen	8. Magnesium
2. Silicon	9. Chlorine
3. Aluminum	10. Hydrogen
4. Iron	11. Titanium
5. Calcium	12. Phosphorus
6. Sodium	13. Carbon
7. Potassium	

FIGURE 5–1

SYMBOLS FOR IMPORTANT ELEMENTS

Aluminum	Al	Iron	Fe	Tin	Sn
Barium	Ba	Krypton	Kr	Titanium	Ti
Bismuth	Bi	Lead	Pb	Uranium	U
Boron	B	Magnesium	Mg	Xenon	Xe
Bromine	Br	Manganese	Mn	Zinc	Zn
Cadmium	Cd	Mercury	Hg	Zirconium	Zr
Calcium	Ca	Neon	Ne		
Carbon	C	Nickel	Ni		
Cesium	Cs	Nitrogen	N		
Chlorine	Cl	Oxygen	O		
Chromium	Cr	Phosphorus	P		
Cobalt	Co	Potassium	K		
Copper	Cu	Radium	Ra		
Fluorine	F	Silicon	Si		
Helium	He	Silver	Ag		
Hydrogen	H	Sodium	Na		
Iodine	I	Sulfur	S		

FIGURE 5–2

be seen very frequently. Your instructor will probably recommend that you commit to memory many or all of these. Memorizing lists is a dull task but, considering the amount of time it will save you in looking up symbols later on, it is well worth the effort. Moreover, it is a surprising fact that something once committed to memory can remain with a person for a lifetime.

Now that we know the symbols for a number of elements, let us start to write formulas for compounds. We have looked at two basic types of bonding—ionic and covalent. We found that the ionic bonds occurred between elements that wanted to ˙lose electrons and elements that wanted to gain electrons. The resulting electronic structures were those of the inert gases. The elements that give up electrons become positive ions and are called *electropositive elements.* The ones that gain electrons become negative and are called *electronegative elements.* Electropositive elements are also called *metals* and electronegative elements are called *nonmetals.* In looking at the periodic chart we find the metals generally on the left and the nonmetals generally on the right. The reason that we cannot draw a vertical dividing line between metals and nonmetals is that there is a change in this property from top to bottom as well as from left to right. We have associated metallic character with ability to lose electrons. Now, we know that the farther an electron is from the positive nucleus, the easier it is to remove this electron. If you compare lead, Pb, with the first member of its family, carbon, C, you will say that there are many more shells occupied in the lead atom and that therefore lead's outermost electrons are more easily removed than carbon's. You are correct, and in fact, you know that lead is a metal while carbon is a typical nonmetal. The steps going down from left to right through Columns III to VII separate the metals from the nonmetals. We can say that metallic character *increases* from top to bottom and *decreases* from left to right. This is a useful guide to remember.

Metals react with nonmetals to form ionic compounds. For instance, sodium is found in Column I (the alkali metal family) and chlorine in Column VII (the halogen family). The metal sodium, being electropositive, gives up an electron to the nonmetal chlorine, which is electronegative. The result is the ionic compound sodium chloride. On the other hand, when we consider two electronegative elements reacting with *each other*, we witness a sharing operation with resultant covalent bonding. Let us start our naming system by considering compounds that are combinations of two different elements. These are called *binary compounds*. The first group will be combinations in *ionic compounds*.

BINARY COMPOUNDS OF METALS AND NONMETALS

We saw how sodium and chlorine join to form salt, sodium chloride. Notice that the ending of the name is ide. All binary compounds end in ide. In an ionic compound the metal atom is named first, with the ide ending added onto the stem of the nonmetal's name. When we formed sodium chloride, NaCl, and calcium chloride, $CaCl_2$, we had to keep a balance of the electrons exchanged. A sodium atom lost one electron to a chlorine atom. The result was a single positively charged sodium ion, Na^+, and a single negatively charged chloride ion, Cl^-. Keep in mind that the total charge of the two together is zero. This must be so, since we still have the same total number of protons and electrons. Let's go through that routine again, but with calcium chloride. A calcium atom loses two electrons to two chlorine atoms. The result is a double positively charged calcium ion, Ca^{++}, and two single negatively charged chloride ions, Cl^- and Cl^-. Again the total charge of the collection of ions is zero.

Now, if we have at hand a number of common positive ions and a number of negative ions it will be easy for us to put them together so that the total charge comes out to zero. The naming is also easy. Let us write the formula for an ionic compound made up of the ions potassium, K^+, and sulfide, $S^=$. Since the potassium ion is plus one and the sulfide ion is minus two, we must have two potassium ions for every sulfide ion, or K_2S. The name of the compound is potassium sulfide. That wasn't too bad, but you are probably wondering how you are supposed to know the names and charges of a lot of ions. The periodic chart can help us out here. We recall that the arrangement in the chart is a structural one and that the groupings reflect similarities among the elements. It is a fact that certain families, such as those in Column I of Fig. 5–3, the alkali family, exist in compounds as ions with only one particular charge, while other families can exist as ions with various charges. An example of the latter is iron, Fe, which can exist in compounds as the ferrous ion Fe^{++}, or as the ferric ion Fe^{+++}. Members of the alkali family, such as sodium or potassium, can only exist as a plus one ion, Na^+ or K^+. This is directly related to the electronic structure, for sodium and its alkali relatives have only one s electron in the outermost shell. The loss of this electron gives rise to the plus one ions; we refer to this as an oxidation state of

IONS OF COMMON ELEMENTS IN BINARY IONIC COMPOUNDS

I	II	III	IV	V	VI	VII
$H \rightarrow H^+$					$O \rightarrow O^=$	$F \rightarrow F^-$
$Li \rightarrow Li^+$	$Be \rightarrow Be^{++}$				$S \rightarrow S^=$	$Cl \rightarrow Cl^-$
$Na \rightarrow Na^+$	$Mg \rightarrow Mg^{++}$					$Br \rightarrow Br^-$
$K \rightarrow K^+$	$Ca \rightarrow Ca^{++}$					$I \rightarrow I^-$
$Rb \rightarrow Rb^+$	$Sr \rightarrow Sr^{++}$					
$Cs \rightarrow Cs^+$	$Ba \rightarrow Ba^{++}$					

FIGURE 5–3

plus one. Metals such as iron which occur in the middle of the chart can lose *s* electrons and *d* electrons as well, thus giving rise to the possibility of more than one oxidation *state*. As a matter of fact, the metals in the middle of the chart, the transition elements, are well known for their multiplicity of oxidation states. The elements that do exhibit *fixed* oxidation states can be remembered as follows: Column I yields plus one ions, Column II yields plus two ions, and in *binary* compounds Column VII yields minus one ions, while Column VI yields minus two ions. (See Fig. 5–3.)

Examples of binary ionic compounds that can be formed from the ions in Fig. 5–3 are shown in Fig. 5–4.

Compounds with metals having variable oxidation states are formed as above; the charge on the ion is important in each case. Since iron can exist as Fe^{++} or Fe^{+++}, iron and chlorine can form $FeCl_2$ or $FeCl_3$. The modern way to name these is iron (II) chloride and iron (III) chloride. The traditional names for the ions are ferrous (Fe^{++}) and ferric (Fe^{+++}). Thus, you will still see the names ferrous chloride ($FeCl_2$) and ferric chloride ($FeCl_3$) used. (See Fig. 5–5.)

The new naming system presents the oxidation state of the element in the compound involved and eliminates the need for learning a separate name for each ion. Note that the roman numerals are not necessary for atoms with a fixed oxidation state. Unfortunately, the old naming system will probably be a long time in disappearing, and therefore we have to be familiar with both systems.

You should have no trouble now in naming and writing formulas for binary ionic compounds made from metals from Columns I and II and nonmetals from Columns VI and VII. As for other binary ionic com-

NaBr	Sodium bromide
Li_2O	Lithium oxide
$MgCl_2$	Magnesium chloride
CaS	Calcium sulfide

FIGURE 5–4

	MODERN NAME	OLD NAME
$FeCl_2$	Iron (II) chloride	Ferrous chloride
$FeCl_3$	Iron (III) chloride	Ferric chloride

FIGURE 5–5

pounds, the various oxidation states will have to be memorized or taken from a list. We will talk of this again later when we have finished with a discussion of the formulas and names of binary compounds of non-metallic elements.

BINARY COMPOUNDS OF NONMETALS

Through covalent bonding involving single, double, and triple bonds, a variety of combinations of nonmetals are possible. For instance, carbon and oxygen form CO and CO_2; nitrogen and oxygen form N_2O, NO, NO_2, N_2O_4, and N_2O_5; carbon and chlorine form CCl_4, while phosphorus and chlorine form PCl_3 and PCl_5. The naming of these compounds is very systematic. The prefixes di, tri, tetra, penta, and hexa are used where necessary. If one atom only is indicated, no prefix is necessary. Again the ending is ide. The above examples are named as shown in Fig. 5–6.

CO	Carbon monoxide
CO_2	Carbon dioxide
N_2O	Dinitrogen oxide
NO	Nitrogen oxide
NO_2	Nitrogen dioxide
N_2O_4	Dinitrogen tetroxide
N_2O_5	Dinitrogen pentoxide
CCl_4	Carbon tetrachloride
PCl_3	Phosphorus trichloride
PCl_5	Phosphorus pentachloride

FIGURE 5–6

It must be pointed out that this system of naming is fairly recent and that the reader may come across other less accurate but historically important names that were used for many years and stubbornly resist change. For instance, an anesthetic gas that dentists still employ is N_2O. The older name for it, which is still in use, is nitrous oxide. The newer name, dinitrogen oxide, tells us the composition of the compound, whereas the other name does not.

Now we will look at compounds that contain more than two different elements. To start with, we will consider ionic compounds which contain what we call polyatomic ions.

COMPOUNDS WITH POLYATOMIC IONS

The term polyatomic ion sounds formidable but is really quite simple. It means an ion made up of two or more elements. For instance, there is the sulfate ion, $SO_4^=$. This ion contains a sulfur atom around which are four oxygen atoms covalently attached. This collection of four oxygen atoms and one sulfur atom has two more electrons than protons and hence carries a double negative charge. An example of a polyatomic ion with a positive charge is the ammonium ion, NH_4^+. This unit has four hydrogen atoms covalently attached to a central nitrogen atom. The total number of protons exceeds the number of electrons by one, giving a positive charge of one to the ion.

For the purposes of writing formulas and naming, the polyatomic ions can be *considered* to be simple (monatomic) ions. For instance, the potassium ion, K^+, can be combined with the sulfate ion, $SO_4^=$, to give potassium sulfate, K_2SO_4. Since the sulfate ion is minus two and the potassium ion is plus one, there have to be two potassium ions for each sulfate ion. Likewise, the ammonium ion, NH_4^+, and the chloride ion combine to form ammonium chloride, NH_4Cl. In Fig. 5–7 there is a list of common positive and negative ions (*cations* and *anions*). Learning this list will be a great aid in recognizing and naming chemical formulas. Single combinations of these ions which produce electrical neutrality result in a large number of compounds. When the charges do not balance out readily, we can use the following device: iron (III) ion, Fe^{+++}, and oxide ion, $O^=$, combine to form iron (III) oxide. The formula can be written by making the subscript for the oxygen atoms the same as the

POSITIVE IONS (CATIONS)		NEGATIVE IONS (ANIONS)	
Hydrogen	H^+	Carbonate	$CO_3^=$
Ammonium	NH_4^+	Bicarbonate (hydrogen carbonate)	HCO_3^-
Potassium	K^+	Bromide	Br^-
Aluminum	Al^{+++}	Chloride	Cl^-
Silver	Ag^+	Chlorate	ClO_3^-
Sodium	Na^+	Fluoride	F^-
Cuprous (copper I)	Cu^+	Iodide	I^-
Cupric (copper II)	Cu^{++}	Hydroxide	OH^-
Barium	Ba^{++}	Oxide	$O^=$
Calcium	Ca^{++}	Sulfide	$S^=$
Lead	Pb^{++}	Bisulfide (hydrogen sulfide)	HS^-
Magnesium	Mg^{++}	Nitrate	NO_3^-
Zinc	Zn^{++}	Sulfate	$SO_4^=$
Lithium	Li^+	Bisulfate (hydrogen sulfate)	HSO_4^-
Nickelous (nickel II)	Ni^{++}	Sulfite	$SO_3^=$
Nickelic (nickel III)	Ni^{+++}	Phosphate	$PO_4^{\equiv}$
Ferrous (iron II)	Fe^{++}	Hydrogen phosphate	$HPO_4^=$
Ferric (iron III)	Fe^{+++}	Dihydrogen phosphate	$H_2PO_4^-$
		Permanganate	MnO_4^-
		Chromate	$CrO_4^=$

FIGURE 5–7

charge on the iron and the subscript for the iron atom the same as the charge on the oxygen atom. For an example, see Fig. 5–8. Another example is magnesium phosphate, as shown in Fig. 5–9. Notice that parentheses are placed around the phosphate ion for clarity. For compounds that contain a metal ion, hydrogen, and a polyatomic negative ion, the di, tri, etc., prefixes are used. For example, Na_2HPO_4 is disodium hydrogen phosphate and NaH_2PO_4 is sodium dihydrogen phosphate. Baking soda, $NaHCO_3$, is called sodium hydrogen carbonate, but more commonly, sodium bicarbonate.

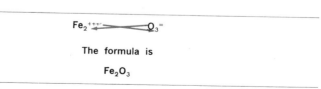

The formula is

Fe_2O_3

FIGURE 5–8   IRON (III) OXIDE

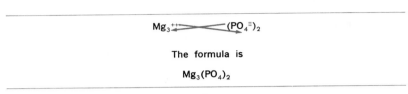

The formula is

$Mg_3(PO_4)_2$

FIGURE 5–9   MAGNESIUM PHOSPHATE

ACIDS

A special situation exists in the naming of acids, such as HCl and HNO_3. Note that the formula for an acid starts with hydrogen. In the pure state these are called hydrogen chloride and hydrogen nitrate. However, when they are dissolved in water, they ionize and release the hydrogen ions which are characteristic of acids. In the water solution these acids are called hydrochloric acid and nitric acid. Similarly, in water solution, hydrogen sulfite and hydrogen sulfate become sulfurous acid and sulfuric acid. Other acids are named similarly.

ORGANIC COMPOUNDS

We have now covered formulas and naming for binary compounds of metals and nonmetals, binary compounds of nonmetals, and compounds of polyatomic ions. This covers a very large percentage of the names and formulas that we will encounter. For special families of compounds—for instance, carbon compounds—there are specific naming systems. Since carbon atoms can attach to each other as well as to other atoms, a large variety of structures is possible. Since this type of construction is present in living things, this area of chemistry is called organic chemistry. The structures can be classified into various families or series depending on the arrangements of atoms present. For example, a series of carbon-hydrogen atoms (hydrocarbon series) is named as shown in Fig. 5–10.

Each of these structures is called a radical. You will note that since carbon has four electrons in its outer shell, it is capable of forming four bonds. The dash to the right of each of the above groupings represents

CH_3-	Methyl
CH_3-CH_2-	Ethyl
$CH_3-CH_2-CH_2-$	Propyl
$CH_3-CH_2-CH_2-CH_2-$	Butyl

FIGURE 5–10

a bond that can be made to some other atom not shown. Other groupings of atoms represent families, as shown in Fig. 5–11.

Note that the dash represents as before a bond that is made to some other atom. Such groupings as these are called *functional groups*. Combinations of radicals and functional groups correspond to actual compounds, as shown in Fig. 5–12.

Radicals and functional groups do not exist by themselves. They are considered separate entities only for the purpose of naming. You can see that the structures of organic compounds lend themselves to a very systematic classification. Indeed, there is a quite detailed modern system for naming organic compounds. It involves the types of functional groups, the number of carbon atoms involved, and the relative positions of the various atoms. As we have observed with the binary compounds,

$-OH$	Alcohol family
$-NH_2$	Amine family

FIGURE 5–11

CH_3-OH	CH_3-CH_2-OH	etc.
Methyl alcohol	Ethyl alcohol	
CH_3-NH_2	$CH_3-CH_2-NH_2$	etc.
Methyl amine	Ethyl amine	

FIGURE 5–12

the new naming system here overlaps the older common names. For instance, methyl alcohol and ethyl alcohol are the common or trivial names. They should more correctly be called methanol and ethanol. The complete transition to the newer naming system in chemistry will doubt-less take a long time. We now have a sufficient foundation on which to build our knowledge of formulas and naming, and as we study the applied areas of chemistry we will learn additional structures and names.

WRITING EQUATIONS

Having completed our introduction to the naming of compounds and the writing of formulas, we should proceed to a consideration of the basics of writing equations. First, why should we write equations at all, and what does an equation represent? When a chemical reaction takes place, there is a rearrangement of atoms. We, of course, are interested in knowing what rearrangement has taken place. If we attempted to write out the names of the starting materials and the names of the products, the result would be a cumbersome set of words. Again a shorthand method is necessary for quick interpretation. We therefore express the starting materials and the products in terms of their formulas.

Now we must also keep in mind that for all intents and purposes no mass is gained or lost in a chemical reaction. In other words, all the atoms that we start with must be found in the products, regardless of the rearrrangement. For instance, sodium metal reacts with chlorine to form salt, sodium chloride. Remember that chlorine exists as a diatomic molecule in order to have the argon structure. Let us write the equation for this reaction stepwise. First, write the formulas for the starting materials with a plus sign between them. Follow this with an arrow, meaning "yields," and the formula for the product.

Inspection of step (1) in Fig. 5–13 reveals that the way we have written the equation so far seems to indicate that we started with two atoms of chlorine and ended up with only one. You know, of course, that the chlorine atoms must gain one electron each from two sodium atoms. This results in a pair each of sodium and chloride ions. To represent this in our equation, Fig. 5–14, we use numbers in front of the formulas. These numbers are called *coefficients*.

Be sure to notice the difference between a subscript and a coefficient. In the chlorine molecule there are two atoms of chlorine bonded

STEP 1	Na sodium atom	+	CL$_2$ chlorine molecule	→	NaCl sodium ion plus chloride ion

FIGURE 5–13

together—hence the subscript 2. The molecule is constructed this way, and we cannot change this subscript. However, a coefficient in front of a formula means we have two or three (or whatever number is indicated) of the unit described by the formula. The 2 in front of the sodium formula, for instance, refers to two atoms of sodium, and the 2 in front of NaCl refers to two sodium ions and two chloride ions. Coefficients can vary from one equation to another, whereas the subscripts for a particular structure can never vary. The equation represented in step (1) is referred to as "unbalanced," while the equation in step (2) is balanced. In reactions, there is generally an exchange of energy and often the equation is written so as to indicate this. If a reaction liberates energy, we say that it is *exothermic*; if it absorbs energy, it is *endothermic*. The above reaction is strongly exothermic and could be indicated as shown in Fig. 5–15, step (3).

If a reaction is endothermic, the energy term will be found on the left side of the equation. Although step (3) is the most complete way to represent a reaction, throughout this text equations will usually be written as in step (2). Other examples of equations written stepwise are as shown in Fig. 5–16.

STEP 2	2Na two sodium atoms	+	Cl$_2$ chlorine molecule	→	2NaCl two sodium ions and two chloride ions

FIGURE 5–14

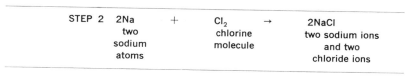

STEP 3 $2Na + Cl_2 \rightarrow 2NaCl + energy$

FIGURE 5–15

STEP 1	H_2 hydrogen molecule	+	Cl_2 chlorine molecule	→	HCl hydrogen chloride molecule
STEP 2	H_2 hydrogen molecule	+	Cl_2 chlorine molecule	→	2HCl two hydrogen chloride molecules
STEP 1	H_2 hydrogen molecule	+	O_2 oxygen molecule	→	H_2O water molecule
STEP 2	$2H_2$ two hydrogen molecules	+	O_2 oxygen molecule	→	$2H_2O$ two water molecules

FIGURE 5–16

In selecting the proper coefficients needed to balance an equation, a trial and error method can often be used. To check the validity of the balancing, you need only "count up" the number of atoms on each side of the arrow. For the above equations, the balance in terms of atoms is as follows:

1.	2NA 2 sodium atoms	+	CL_2 2 chlorine atoms	→	2NaCl 2 sodium atoms 2 chlorine atoms
total	2 Na atoms	+	2 Cl atoms	→	2 Na atoms + 2 Cl atoms
2.	H_2 2 hydrogen atoms	+	CL_2 2 chlorine atoms	→	2HCl 2 hydrogen atoms 2 chlorine atoms
total	2 H atoms	+	2 Cl atoms	→	2 H atoms + 2 Cl atoms
3.	$2H_2$ 4 hydrogen atoms	+	O_2 2 oxygen atoms	→	$2H_2O$ 4 hydrogen atoms 2 oxygen atoms
total	4 H atoms	+	2 O atoms	→	4 H atoms + 2 O atoms

FIGURE 5–17

When balancing equations, if your bookkeeping on the atoms does not balance out, you have done something wrong. Go back and check the formulas and then the coefficients.

At this point your basic information about the atoms, how they stick together, how we represent formulas and reactions, and how we name the compounds involved is sufficient to allow us to discuss the various applied and research fields of the chemist. I want you to appreciate what the chemist does, the types of research that are being pursued, and the role of chemistry in topics of great importance to every citizen. Throughout these discussions, where it is possible, we will apply and expand the basic principles we have covered in these beginning chapters.

QUESTIONS AND PROJECTS

1. Look up the percentage compositions of the 13 most abundant elements in the earth's crust.

2. Write chemical symbols side by side for the following elements:
a. Barium, sodium, sodium
b. Sulfur, phosphorus, oxygen, oxygen, nitrogen
c. Thorium, oxygen, radon
d. Titanium, rhenium, sulfur
e. Lanthanium, yttrium, oxygen, fluorine, fluorine

3. Write from memory the symbols for
a. Boron
b. Carbon
c. Copper
d. Fluorine
e. Tin
f. Nitrogen
g. Magnesium
h. Potassium
i. Silver
j. Sodium

4. Give from memory the names of
a. Al
b. Bi
c. Mn
d. P
e. S
f. Cl
g. Zn
h. Hg
i. Pb
j. Cr

5. Does electronegativity vary in the periodic chart
a. From left to right?
b. From top to bottom?
Explain.

6. In the periodic chart where are the metals located? The nonmetals?

7. Name 10 different binary ionic compounds and write formulas for them.

8. Write formulas for
a. Iron (II) sulfate
b. Magnesium chlorate
c. Zinc oxide
d. Barium nitrate
e. Sodium phosphate
f. Calcium iodide
g. Dinitrogen trioxide
h. Disodium hydrogen phosphate
i. Hydrogen sulfate
j. Carbon tetrachloride

9. Give names for
a. $Cu(NO_3)_2$
b. $NaHCO_3$
c. $NiCrO_4$
d. $AgCl$
e. Li_2SO_3
f. H_2SO_3
g. PCl_3
h. SO_2
i. $CaSO_4$
j. $KMnO_4$

10. Write balanced equations for the following:
a. Zinc plus sulfuric acid yields zinc sulfate plus hydrogen.
b. Zinc plus hydrochloric acid yields zinc chloride plus hydrogen.
c. Silver nitrate plus calcium chloride yields silver chloride plus calcium nitrate.
d. Calcium plus chlorine yields calcium chloride.
e. Sodium hydrogen carbonate plus hydrochloric acid yields water, carbon dioxide, and sodium chloride.

11. How does metallic character vary in the periodic table? Give an example of a family in which the first and last member are distinctly different in metallic character.

12. Summarize the rules for naming simple inorganic compounds.

13. Explain what is meant by organic radicals and functional groups. Give examples.

14. What is an endothermic reaction? An exothermic reaction? How could this be indicated in an equation? Give an example of each.

15. A neutralization is a chemical reaction which involves an acid and a base. The products are water and a salt. For instance, a water solution of hydrochloric acid, HCl, reacts with potassium hydroxide, KOH, to yield water, H_2O, and a salt, potassium chloride, KCL. Write balanced equations for five neutralization reactions.

6

RESEARCH IN UNIVERSITIES

The student who majors in chemistry and who desires to obtain an advanced degree, usually a Ph.D., will go to a graduate school. This graduate school may or may not be attached to the undergraduate school that the student attended. Generally, it is more rewarding for the student to leave his undergraduate campus and to be exposed to new teachers, different approaches, and a new group of students.

One of the most important things the advanced degree candidate in chemistry must do is to perform a research project. Ph.D. doesn't really mean "piled higher and deeper." It signifies that the holder is capable of initiating and completing independent research. At graduate school, there must be guidance and supervision in the research problem; therefore, the student selects one of the professors as a thesis advisor. Usually the student has some idea about which field of chemistry he would like to pursue; consequently, he will interview the various professors who are engaged in research in that field.

Having selected an advisor and a topic, the graduate student will embark upon his research problem, which may last for several years. At the end of that time, having completed all the other requirements for graduation, he will write and submit his thesis for examination and approval. If approved, generally by a committee of professors, the student will then receive his degree.

The research work performed for the thesis is usually published in a chemical journal, thus adding to our fund of scientific information. Work that has been accurately performed and recorded need not be repeated. In this way, we are able to build on our knowledge and continue to expand our understanding of nature.

PUBLISH OR PERISH

Since results of experimentation are published, there is a way of measuring the research activity of various schools. Indeed, for better or for worse, the volume of publications from a college or university has become a status symbol. The problem of "publish or perish" is with us. I have maintained that chemistry is an experimental science and that research is an absolute necessity. On the other hand, I would like to point out some problems that can be caused by a headlong rush toward research.

Many of the larger schools have decided to pour funds into graduate school equipment, buildings, and staff, with the corresponding neglect of the undergraduate division. It must be kept in mind that graduate schools are servicing a very small percentage of the total student body. Most of the students, by far, are enrolled in undergraduate curricula. Where experienced professors used to spend considerable time lecturing and counseling students, now we find that, because of the pressure to maintain their individual status and the school's status, they must spend their time producing a disproportionate amount of print.

The undergraduate students in many cases are lectured by inexperienced graduate students rather than by professors. The beginning chemistry courses, which in the author's opinion are the most important, are the ones that are being neglected the most. At many schools the material is "thrown" at the students, who must "sink or swim." Very outstanding students will learn, whether or not there is an instructor, but most need help, guidance, and inspiration. The publish or perish attitude is, without a doubt, hurting instruction on the undergraduate level, both in chemistry and in other fields. The unrest at many campuses where the undergraduate student feels that he is only part of a "factory" can be traced in large part to publish or perish. Admittedly, a school that performs no research is in an unhealthy condition, but a school that performs so much research that it neglects good teaching and the welfare of the student is also in trouble. Somehow a way must be developed to measure and recognize a school for excellence in research *and* teaching.

Let us consider the types of research that are performed in schools. (I must point out that not all research is performed on the graduate level. Many seniors execute outstanding research problems. At some schools the chemistry major is required to do a "senior thesis." At other schools he may do it on a voluntary "honors" basis.) In "pure" or "basic" research, the chemist is interested mainly in facts. He would like to know the underlying reasons for reactions that take place, structures that are formed, and properties that are observed. These studies and their results often appear to have no practical or tangible value. In fact, many times it would appear that the basic research chemist is "playing games" with atoms and molecules. Despite the fact that there are no immediate goals for this type of research, it is probably the most valuable research being performed. Experiments that explain the why and wherefore of various reactions may sometime in the future provide the key to long-standing practical problems. For instance, a basic research chemist in a university might develop a method for preparing some new and complex compound with no use at that time. Perhaps years later a similar structure might be discovered in an enzyme system of the human body. The method of preparation and the properties observed years before by the basic research chemist might provide the solution to the mechanism of an important bodily process.

RESEARCH SUPPORT

Financing basic research in graduate schools is, of course, an important and difficult problem. Buildings, staff, equipment, and services must be provided. The schools, both private and state-supported, bear a large portion of the expense, while some of the research programs are supported by government agencies such as the National Science Foundation.

Financing problems often lead schools into another type of research, referred to as *applied research*. While there is no distinct line dividing "pure" and "applied" research, generally pure research is as I have just described it, while applied research is experimentation that has an immediate, tangible goal. Various industries have research problems which they may not have the time, equipment, or experience to pursue. They are happy to make grants to universities that will undertake such studies. For the sponsoring companies, such grants generally represent tax deductions, a source of advertising, and good public relations. Many

FIGURE 6–1   MODELING A PROTEIN MOLECULE AT INDIANA UNIVERSITY. (*BY PERMISSION OF INDIANA UNIVERSITY.*)

times the companies allow the professor and his research students to perform basic research with "no strings attached." However, generally they want certain scientific questions answered within a reasonable length of time.

Private industry is not alone in encouraging applied university research. Government agencies with specific objectives in areas such as space travel, aeronautics, and warfare grant contracts not only to firms but also to schools. They are looking for new rocket fuels, propellants, insulation for space vehicles, solar batteries, and so on. Not long ago, graduate school research was almost all "pure." Today, however, although applied research is still frowned upon by many professors and college presidents, it appears to be here to stay.

Basic research, although usually long-range, is sometimes put to use at once. Many private companies will encourage university research staffs to submit new compounds prepared in the school laboratories for various screening tests. For instance, some companies engaged in producing agricultural chemicals routinely screen university-prepared compounds for use as insecticides, virucides, growth regulators, fungicides, etc. In addition, nonprofit organizations, such as the Sloan-Kettering Institute for Cancer Research, will examine new compounds from universities and other sources in search of solutions to their particular problems.

A SUGAR-FREE DISCOVERY

Occasionally, basic research accidentally produces a useful product. A graduate student not long ago was working on a special group of nitrogen-containing compounds. He happened to taste one of them; it was very sweet. After considerable testing and evaluation by a pharmaceutical company, this compound, N-cyclohexyl sulfamic acid, became the precursor of the cyclamates, artificial sweeteners which were consumed for over fifteen years. Since cyclamates were found to cause cancer in rats, the U.S. government and others have banned their use. In the next chapter, we will consider industrial research, which, in order to remain in a healthy economic condition, *must* produce useful results.

QUESTIONS AND PROJECTS

1. Make a list of the universities in your state that offer graduate training in chemistry.

2. For each of the above universities, determine approximately how many graduate students and how many undergraduate students are enrolled
a. In chemistry
b. In all fields

3. For one of the above universities, obtain a rough estimate of
a. How many full-time faculty members teach in the graduate school
b. How many full-time faculty members teach in the undergraduate school

4. For the same university as in question 3, determine the approximate budget for
a. The graduate school
b. The undergraduate school

5. In your opinion does this university have a publish-or-perish attitude? If so, is it harmful to the undergraduate program?

6. Describe in general terms a *basic* research problem in chemistry that is currently being carried out at some university. How is the project financed?

7. Describe in general terms an *applied* research problem in chemistry that is currently being carried out at some university. How is the project financed?

8. Do you feel that private or state-supported universities should sponsor defense research programs? Why?

9. In your opinion, should universities be involved in scientific research? If not, why not? If so, what types of research?

10. Do you think that unrest on campuses is related to the publish-or-perish attitude? Give an example, if you can.

11. Should a student seeking an advanced degree stay at his undergraduate campus or attend a different school? Discuss.

12. Why is a graduate degree important? Should the importance of such degrees be deemphasized?

13. If defense research is eliminated from universities, who should conduct this work, if it is to continue?

14. Should research in universities be aimed primarily at training students or at some other goal? If the former, how can it be encouraged?

15. Find out approximately how many chemistry journals there are now and how many there were 10 years ago.

7

RESEARCH
IN
INDUSTRY

We have found that the usual type of research performed in our colleges and universities has no particular emphasis on tangible or monetary results. Schools, despite the fact that they are very large operations handling budgets in the millions of dollars, are nonprofit organizations. On the other hand, industry is in business to make money. A company must provide products or services that can be sold for a profit. The output of chemical concerns ranges from basic raw materials to finished products that are eventually sold to individuals. Any product, however, that is worth selling by one company is also worth duplication and selling by another. Although government patents may afford temporary protection, the chemical producer must continually upgrade, revise, and add to his products to keep ahead of competition. This is accomplished through industrial research.

THE TELEVISION SCIENTIST

The majority of the public has received a distorted picture of industrial research through television advertising. The little man in the white coat, surrounded by acres of glassware, is playing some sort of game with a cigarette-smoking apparatus or is listening for the alarm bell in his odor machine. This is what the advertising media want us to believe a research chemist does. Add to this the pseudoscientific tests, the trick photography, and the clever wording that the ads employ, and the research chemist looks pretty inferior.

Anyone who takes a moment to study the various "scientific ads" that appear on television will quickly realize that most of them are rigged to produce false confidence in the buyers of the product. Advertising is a necessary evil involved in the transfer of the finished product from the manufacturer to the consumer. Unfortunately, it is usually true that effective promotion is more important than the quality of the item, as far as sales are concerned. Because of the very high cost of newspaper, radio, and especially television ads, only the business with large amounts of capital can sell its products. The result is that many exceptional inventions by individuals are lost to the public.

PRODUCT DEVELOPMENT

Let us consider industrial research as it really takes place. Research departments vary from one company to another, but certain types of operations are common to most of them. We will first discuss product development. This usually involves the mixing together of various "active" and "inert" ingredients into a finished product. Some scientists might argue that this is really not research, since it involves only formulating the compounds rather than discovering new and useful structures.

However, product development requires all the resources of trained research personnel and can present very difficult scientific problems, some of which may require years for solution. Every company that manufactures a product must have some sort of product development. The company may not be large enough to afford basic research, but it must conduct product development to keep its items competitive. As a matter of fact, many companies which would like to convey the impression that they have a very complete research department have in reality only a product development group.

The problems involved in this area are many. The chemist is likely to be given some active ingredient which may have a special property— insecticidal, detergent, disinfectant, wax, antiperspirant, or other. He must determine in what concentration this active ingredient will be most effective. He must also decide how the product is to be delivered, whether as a solid, solution, suspension, aerosol, or otherwise. From a variety of packages available, he must make a selection, keeping in mind such things as appropriate type of delivery for the particular item, stability of the product, corrosion, compatibility with propellant, container linings, and cost. If the product is visible to the customer, it must have a pleasing appearance. For instance, settling out of ingredients or separating of liquid layers is unacceptable. A personal product, such as a deodorant, cosmetic, or detergent, must have special qualities. Certain items that come under the Food and Drug Act now require extensive testing on the part of the manufacturer to assure effectiveness and safety for the user of the product. Many laboratory and clinical tests involving animals and humans must be performed to the satisfaction of the Food and Drug Administration before the product can be put on sale. In addition to this, a personal item must have a faultless appearance and a pleasant odor. Such qualities often demand special laboratories. For example, perfuming must be conducted in a laboratory removed from all other odors. The chemist who is skilled at mixing perfumes to match existing odors or who creates new odors, often with the added burden of masking chemical odors already present in a product, is a very talented and useful member of the research team. Another example of a special lab needed for product development is a cosmetic powder lab. Here the chemist must produce various delicate shades under carefully controlled lighting that simulates indoor and outdoor illumination. This chemist, in addition to helping the product-development group, will also probably act as a production-control man, checking the day-to-day cosmetic output for proper color and texture.

THE ANALYTICAL LABORATORY

Another very important part of a research department is the analytical laboratory. Here are performed all sorts of analyses on the company's raw materials, research compounds, and intermediate and finished products. The producer must be sure that the raw materials he purchases have the purity specified by the supplier, and, of course, the quality of his own product must be known. Many products are required by law to carry on the label a list of the ingredients, and items such as drugs must conform to an exact percentage composition. The day-to-day analysis of the company's products may be performed by a "control laboratory" under the direction of the production department, rather than by the analytical lab. Whichever way it is administratively set up, the control lab will work very closely with the analytical lab since the procedures and equipment are very similar.

A large and important function of the analytical laboratory is the analysis of competitors' products. Very few products are effectively protected by patents, and a great number of products are very similar to one another. As a matter of fact, the average person would be very unhappy to learn that the chemicals in most household products are worth less than the container. Two products may be almost identical in composition, but one may sell better than the other by virtue of a well-known trademark, widespread advertising, free-sample campaigns, or aggressive salesmanship. It is the expense incurred during the sale and advertising of a product that keeps the prices up so high. For instance, most liquid detergents cost the manufacturer a few cents a quart. Much of the difference between cost and sales price is due to promotion and sales cost. There is, of course, a profit for the successful producer. Any small manufacturer, who could devise a way to provide real "factory-to-you" products, thus eliminating the advertising and sales cost, would give the very large chemical producers serious competition.

PRODUCT EVALUATION

From the analytical lab, we will cross over to another area called product testing or product evaluation. This may be an independent area, or it may be part of product development. A new or revised product, once conceived and put together with the various ingredients designed to make it effective, stable, and pleasing to the consumer, must undergo tests to determine its effectiveness and acceptability. These may range from simple laboratory tests, which try to simulate real use conditions, to actual field tests. A women's hair product, for instance, should not develop static electricity which makes the hair stand on end. Fairly simple laboratory tests can be arranged to measure the amount of charge developed in bits of hair treated with the samples under consideration. For final tests on products of real promise, a company will probably have its own beauty parlor and experiment on volunteers. (Wigs are usually available for women who have taken part in unsuccessful tests.)

For agricultural compounds, evaluation testing is performed on live plants. Companies may either have their own farms and greenhouses, or they may contract for this testing. Drugs are required by law to undergo extensive laboratory and clinical testing to determine effectiveness and to reveal any dangerous side effects. A firm involved in dishwashing and laundry detergents will have some laboratory tests, which simulate practical use conditions, and will also have a "home laundry" of its own. For instance, in the laboratory there are tests which reveal how well detergents can reduce *surface tension*. Water molecules are attracted to one another, and surface tension is a measure of how tightly they "stick together." A surface-active agent is one which breaks down this surface tension and gets water to stick to other things such as dirt, dried-up eggs, and clothes. The effectiveness of a laundry detergent can be gauged by washing swatches of dirty clothes in a laboratory instrument and then measuring the amount of light reflected from the washed pieces. Final testing is performed with actual clothes in the firm's home laundry. It is very useful and very saving of time if a simple, quick laboratory test can be devised to evaluate a product. However, it is often very difficult to simulate conditions of use and thus obtain a valid result. The alternative is to resort to actual conditions. Sometimes companies without field-testing facilities of their own will hire consumer research firms to do the evaluating for them.

PACKAGING RESEARCH

An area that is frequently taken for granted is packaging research. There are many types of individual containers with their corresponding problems. Shall the container be cardboard, glass, plastic, metal, or paper? Is the product corrosive or sensitive to moisture, heat, cold, or aging? Should the product be delivered by shaking, spraying, squirting, or pouring? Will the powdered product settle too much in the box? Will the smaller particles separate from the larger? Is there a dust problem? Will the product clog the spray nozzle? Will the product rust the container and become discolored? What type of lining should be used to prevent corrosion? Are the individual containers and the "overpak" strong enough to withstand the weight of many other cases and the rigors of shipping? These are a few of the questions that face the packaging research chemist every day. Containers, which vary a great deal in price, can control the decision to produce or not to produce a particular item.

BASIC RESEARCH

We finally come to the area of research that is common to both schools and industry—basic research. A chemist performing basic research in industry is often given a great deal of freedom in choosing the problem that he would like to study. The chemist usually is not required to produce tangible, monetary results. The gamble is that over a period of time his basic research will produce something very new, very startling, and also very remunerative. For example, a chemist might be studying the exact mechanism of hair curling, and over a period of years he might come up with a complete picture of the mechanism of the action. Understanding the mechanism, he might then prepare a new hair curler, completely different in structure and much more effective in action than

FIGURE 7–1   DETERGENT RESEARCH. (BY PERMISSION OF WYANDOTTE CHEM-
ICALS CORPORATION.)

any of its competitors. Unfortunately, since basic research does not
bring any immediate results and since it is very costly, only the largest
of companies engage in it.

FROM BASIC RESEARCH TO FINISHED PRODUCT

It would be interesting to follow a chemical compound all the way from
the basic research laboratory to final production. Let us assume that a
discovery has been made in the basic lab and that the structure involved

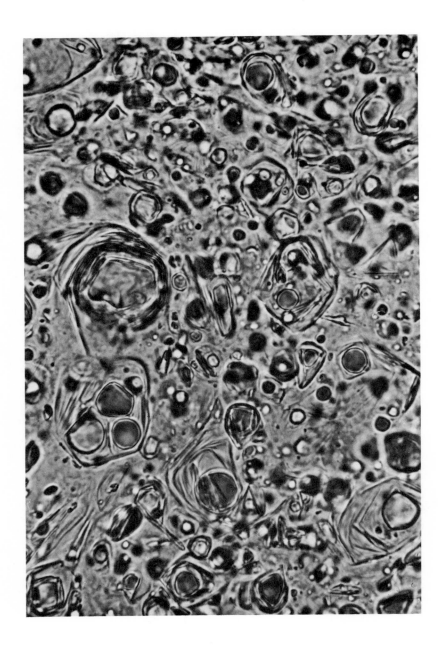

FIGURE 7–2   HAND LOTION, AN EMULSION, AS SEEN UNDER THE MICROSCOPE. *(COURTESY OF ERIC GRAVE.)*

has a valuable property of some sort. The effectiveness of the compound has already been established by various initial product-evaluation tests. The material is sent to the product development lab for proper compounding. Depending on what application is involved, certain ingredients will probably be added to the active ingredient. Many times an added ingredient will enhance the basic effectiveness of the active material.

If the product must have a water base and the liquid ingredients will not dissolve in water, a surface-active agent will have to be selected to bring about emulsification. Emulsification, as opposed to a true solution, in which the dissolved particles are of molecular size, is a condition in which groups of molecules are attracted to the solvent and are thus kept from settling out. Milk, water-base household paints, and floor polishes are examples of emulsions.

The product may need a dye, a perfume, a disinfectant, or other additive. After the complete formulation is determined, its effectiveness must be tested. If the compound shows promise, a container is selected and field testing commences. The product development lab will prepare, or will supervise the preparation of, small batches of the final product. These will be packaged and given final field testing under actual use conditions. If the results are favorable, the product is then ready for production. But here a big step must be taken—from the laboratory with its small intricate pieces of equipment, where cost of reagents and processes are of little concern, to the cost-conscious production department with its huge mixing tanks, industrial pumps, and reactors. Enter the chemical engineer. He must design a process involving perhaps tens of thousands of gallons of mix which will deliver the same quality that the laboratory chemist has achieved in volumes of pints and quarts. To bridge this gap, the chemical engineer often sets up a "pilot plant," or a miniature production plant. In the pilot plant, he uses tanks, reactors, stainless steel pipes, high-pressure pumps, or whatever equipment he feels will be necessary for actual plant operation. Everything is "stepped down" in size. If the engineer can make the product successfully here, he is ready for a trial production "run." After any kinks have been worked out of the actual plant process, the material is ready for continued production. Keep in mind that all through these steps all areas of research, engineering, sales, advertising, and consumer studies pool their resources and work together as a team.

In some of the following chapters we will examine certain specific chemical industries. We will witness some of their remarkable successes as well as some of the problems they have created.

QUESTIONS AND PROJECTS

1. Select a common household chemical product. Find out the ingredients present and describe the various steps the company probably went through to develop the product.

2. Give an example of a poor package and suggest how it could be improved.

3. If possible, visit a company with a chemical research department and describe what you see.

4. Give a review of the film you saw on industrial research.

5. Do you think it is economically more rewarding for a chemical company to engage in basic research and product development or in product development only?

6. If you could find out the exact composition of a leading chemical product, do you feel that you should have the right to copy that formula and sell it under a different name?

7. Which discoveries are patentable and which are not?

8. What protection does a trademark afford?

9. "Shelf life" refers to how long a product can be stored before spoilage or decomposition takes place. Temperature and humidity are often factors. As a product-development director, how would you determine this property?

10. Packages are often given code numbers that indicate date and location of production. Samples of each production batch are carefully stored away. Why do you suppose this is done?

11. Tell about a television ad that you think is scientifically misleading.

12. Name as many different types of packaging for chemical products as you can.

13. Find out the cost of

a. Running a one-minute ad on television

b. Running a half-page ad in a city newspaper

c. Sponsoring a 1-minute ad on a radio station

14. Invent a new chemical product and tell how you would test it and develop it into a salable item.

15. Describe

a. Emulsion

b. Surface tension

c. Aerosol

d. Active ingredient

e. Inert ingredient

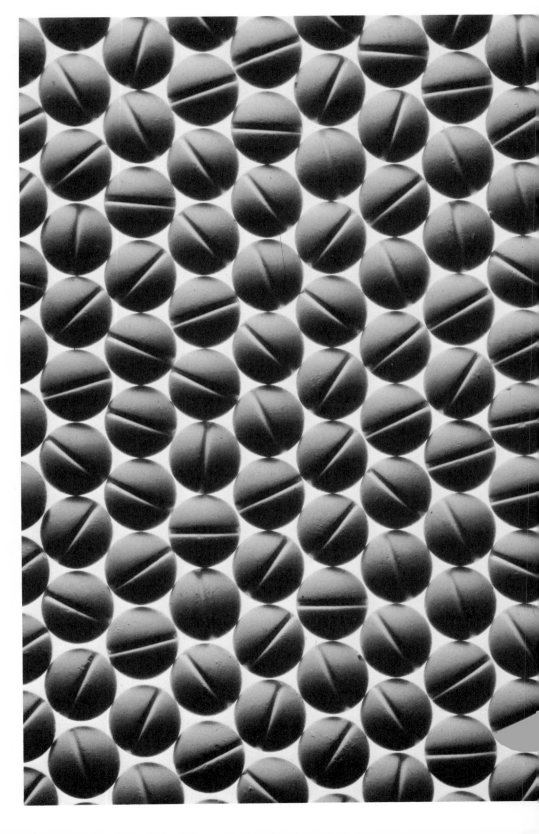

8

DRUGS AND CLINICAL CHEMISTRY

Having taken a bird's-eye view of industrial research, let us now focus on a specific area which is of great interest to all of us. Chemical and medical research have combined to provide us with some wonderful new drugs. Many diseases and conditions that we used to take for granted have become things of the past. Polio, which used to be such a killer, is now essentially under control, and current research and development is very close to producing an effective anti-leukemia agent. Indeed, it is hard to estimate our debt to the dedicated and talented workers in this field.

Drug research is carried out in various places—in schools, government-supported agencies, nonprofit organizations, and drug companies.

Although significant discoveries may take place in any of these areas, only the drug company will carry a discovery through to the production stage. One very obvious reason for this is the tremendous expense that is involved in the testing, evaluation, and manufacture of a pharmaceutical item.

The average person will never take part in drug research, but he should know generally how this research is conducted, how well his safety is protected or how much it is endangered, and how he personally can influence the situation. Drug regulations may be so strict that drug development time may be unduly extended. On the other hand, drug regulations may be too loose, thus creating a possible hazard. Whatever your decision after reading this chapter, you should continue to keep informed and, if necessary, make your feelings known to the proper authorities, in particular the U.S. Department of Health, Education and Welfare.

DISCOVERY TO DRUGSTORE

Let us follow the path of a new drug from its initial discovery to its final production. The research chemist may be studying a particular harmful organism or a certain physical problem, such as high blood pressure. In any event, let us assume that he has discovered a structure or combination of structures that shows promise. Simple laboratory tests are performed first, followed by animal testing. The animals tested usually range from mice and rats to rabbits, dogs, and monkeys.

Safety as well as effectiveness of product must be demonstrated. Unfortunately, reactions that drugs produce in animals are not always translatable to humans. Therefore, human testing under carefully controlled conditions must take place before the product can be released. It is at this point that the public first needs protection. Certainly, no drug company, hospital, or doctor would intentionally administer anything harmful to a volunteer or patient, but even in the best of research programs things can go wrong. Add to this the enthusiasm of a drug producer who is anxious to be the first on the market with a new and effective drug. Millions of dollars in potential sales might encourage him to rush the research and cut a few corners so that production can start promptly. Pushing the research at too fast a pace has led to some serious mistakes.

Before human testing can begin, the company must file a new-drug application with the Food and Drug Administration, which is part of the Department of Health, Education and Welfare. Today, due to some of the errors of the past, the regulations of the FDA are stricter than ever before. The drug producer must present voluminous data on laboratory and animal testing before even limited human testing can begin. He must disclose the nature and method of manufacture of the drug, his plan for clinical evaluation, and the identity and qualifications of doctors participating in the research. Safety and effectiveness of the drug must be demonstrated before final approval is given.

DRUG MISHAPS

The reader might feel this to be a lot of bureaucratic harassment standing in the way of valuable research. Certainly the patient who is waiting for a drug that is still under development and not yet available will find it intolerable. However, keep in mind that the FDA, a regulating agency, was established by the people and that the new stricter regulations were demanded by the public. A brief review of a few outstanding cases will present the other side of the picture.

Before the advent of the wonder drugs, sulfanilamide was in wide use. One producer decided to sell the product as a solution to be injected. He used a solvent without either checking its toxicity or bothering to test it. Over 100 people were killed before the product was recalled from the market. The food and drug regulations, which at that time were too weak to prevent this tragedy, were promptly revised.

THALIDOMIDE TRAGEDY

More recent and more widespread was the case of the sleeping pill thalidomide. A United States drug company made application to market a new drug that would act as a sleeping pill and, further, would treat "morning sickness." At that time (1960–1962), the FDA regulations did not require as much initial data, did not require that effectiveness of claims be substantiated, and did not require detailed records of clinical programs. However, Dr. Frances Kelsey, the very diligent head of the Investigating Drug Branch of the FDA, on learning from a foreign source that there was a side effect on the nervous system of patients who took the drug repeatedly, suspected a problem with pregnant women. She had previously been engaged in research which indicated that nervous disorders would bring about drastic changes in unborn babies. Despite terrific pressure from the drug company, Dr. Kelsey withheld approval. Soon it became known that in Europe thousands of deformed babies had been born to users of thalidomide. The drug company then withdrew its application, and stricter FDA regulations were enacted. While the decision had been pending, the company had distributed samples far and wide, and attempts were made to recall them. But records of cooperating physicians and records of the drug company were so poor that very many users could not be located. Some of the new regulations requiring better records were aimed at preventing a recurrence of this situation.

THE KREBIOZEN CANCER DRUG

Another case, which may not yet be over, is that of the anti-cancer agent Krebiozen. The drug was first announced in 1951 and was refused approval by FDA in 1963. Between these dates there occurred charges, countercharges, political wrangling, scientific studies and disputes, and extreme emotional involvement for families of cancer-stricken patients. The story started in 1951 when two brothers, refugees from Yugoslavia, brought their discovery of Krebiozen to one of this country's most prominent medical scholars and educators. The identity of the drug, contrary to ethical practice, was kept a secret, and testing on humans was initiated without sufficient animal experiments. Other procedures caused considerable criticism. An offer by a drug company to develop the drug was rejected. Adequate records of clinical tests were not being kept, and patients were being charged (as a contribution) up to $9.50 a dose.

When the drug's proponents made application to the FDA in 1961, they submitted a very tiny sample and identified it only with a very general name. They, together with many cancer-stricken families, brought great pressure to bear on the United States government, insisting that the

National Cancer Institute conduct clinical studies, even though there were no animal data to indicate the drug's effectiveness. However, there was established a committee under the guidance of the NCI to study the 504 cases that supposedly demonstrated the value of the drug. The committee, after studying the case histories, concluded that Krebiozen did *not* demonstrate anti-tumor activity in man. The FDA appointed a committee of outstanding scientists to study another sample of the drug submitted by the promoters. The drug was found to be a common chemical, creatine, a normal component in the body and related primarily to muscle contraction. Creatine had been tested some time ago against animal tumors at NCI and had been found ineffective even in very high doses.

THE INFRARED DETECTIVE

The way the drug was identified is a interesting one. The key technique used to prove the drug a rather common chemical was an *infrared spectrogram.*

We will have to jog our memories a bit and go back to Chap. 2 in which we considered various types of light or electromagnetic radiation. Light with high frequency has high energy, and light with low frequency has low energy. Remember that we compared the wave motion of light to the wave motion of the sea, with the number of waves coming in per minute or hour corresponding to frequency. In infrared analyses, light of rather low frequencies (below those of visible red light) is aimed into a sample of the material to be analyzed. Inside the sample, as in all matter, there is constant motion; atoms attached to each other are vibrating and wiggling in various ways. These vibrations and wigglings are occurring at certain frequencies in the infrared range. When light of corresponding frequency strikes the atoms, the light is absorbed and the motion of the atoms is amplified. You can compare this with two waves that are approaching one another. If the crests of the opposing waves come together at the right time, the resulting wave is higher. We call this reinforcement.

When various frequencies of infrared light were passed through the Krebiozen sample, a pen traced a graph indicating which frequencies came through the sample and which were absorbed. This resulting spectrogram matched, within experimental error, the spectrogram of pure creatine.

Even though the FDA in 1963 forbade the interstate shipping of Krebiozen, enforcement was extremely difficult. The government decided to indict the drug proponents on charges of fraud in an attempt to put them out of business. The government pointed out that the apparently worthless drug had been given to some 5,000 patients since 1951. They were asked to make contributions up to $9.50 for a dose worth about 8 cents. The promoters, who made millions of dollars during this period, transplanted their money to Swiss banks. Despite all the evidence, in 1966 the defendants were acquitted by a jury who possibly felt that the drug might have some merit and did not want to kill its chances. Today the drug is still being administered in Illinois, but interstate shipment is prohibited.

THE PILL

Currently, millions of women are taking selected drugs in the form of the various birth-control pills. These are mixtures of the hormones estrogen and progestin, which inhibit ovulation, the movement of an egg down the fallopian tube into the uterus. Without the egg, fertilization cannot take place and pregnancy does not occur. The Pill, under various trade names, has been properly approved by the FDA. However, considerable concern has been expressed about apparent side effects observed since use has become widespread. In particular, blood clots have been reported in a number of users, and a fair number of resulting deaths are said to be related to the Pill. The number of persons experiencing side effects and the number of mortalities, it is feared, are being reported inaccurately or not at all.

Various advisory committees appointed by the FDA continue to study new data relative to any possible danger that might result from use of the pill. Unfortunately, for any drug, it is true that limited clinical data, obtained before drug approval, does not yield enough information to exclude all possibilities, particularly long-range effects. On the other hand, if testing is required for extremely long periods, the public may be needlessly denied the benefit of a very useful drug. Wherever the golden mean may lie, there certainly ought to be regulations that would prevent a near-catastrophe such as the thalidomide affair. There should also be a large and very capable staff of scientific personnel in regulatory agencies such as the FDA. Along with it, there should be an appreciation for the research personnel who want to provide the world with the best remedies in the least possible time.

CLINICAL CHEMISTRY

Closely allied to the field of drugs is clinical chemistry. Before drugs can be administered, problems must be diagnosed; and before the physician can make an accurate diagnosis, he often must have a series of tests run on his patient. Some doctors make a few limited tests in their own offices. There are private clinical laboratories, and of course hospitals have their own complete clinical chemistry departments. If you can arrange to visit the laboratory of an up-to-date hospital, you will certainly be impressed. A large hospital, in connection with a medical school, will probably be performing 40 or 50 different kinds of analyses for a total of about 1,000 each day. A few examples are as follows:

Calcium and magnesium analyses by *atomic absorption:* a method similar to infrared in that certain frequencies of light are absorbed by the calcium or magnesium present in the fluid analyzed

Sodium and potassium analyses by flame photometer: a method in which the sample is introduced into a flame and the characteristic light produced by sodium or potassium is measured

Glucose: *colorimetric analysis* which involves the addition of reagents to the glucose sample. This results in a color, the depth of which indicates the quantity of glucose present

Bicarbonate analysis: in which the bicarbonate reacts with acid to produce carbon dioxide and water. The exact amount of acid used is measured carefully, with the completion of the reaction being indicated by a *pH meter,* an instrument which electronically measures acidity

These are but a few of the many analyses performed, all with modern automatic or semiautomatic instruments. The results are often sent directly to a computer which prints out a card with the patient's identity, his location in the hospital, and the results of the tests. In a situation like this, of course, accuracy is of the utmost importance. Therefore, hospitals are constantly in search of well-trained technicians, research chemists, and engineers to staff these laboratories.

Before leaving this subject, I must note that the expense of constructing, equipping, staffing, and maintaining such a modern laboratory is so great that it must be passed along in the form of higher hospital rates. We all hate to pay bills, but on the other hand, none of us want anything less than the best technical service when we are in need.

QUESTIONS AND PROJECTS

1. In your opinion should drug research and development have more or less governmental supervision? Why?

2. Give the pros and cons of the use of the birth-control pill.

3. Report on the history of the cyclamates and why they were banned. Should the ban order have been issued sooner than it was?

4. Compare the safety, effectiveness, and acceptance of various birth-control methods.

5. Is testing of drugs on animals justified?

6. In some countries mental patients are used in clinical testing. In others, prison convicts can volunteer for such tests. Which system do you prefer and why?

7. Describe the discovery of the birth-control pill.

8. Many drug products are almost identical in composition but are sold at widely varying prices under different trade names. Do you think that drug products should be identified by their actual chemical names or by trade names? Why?

9. Describe the drug research and production program in the film you watched.

10. Visit a clinical laboratory and describe the number and types of tests performed, the testing equipment, and the methods of storing and transmitting results.

11. What methods can you suggest for preventing future thalido-mide-type tragedies?

12. If you had been a member of the "Krebiozen jury" what would have been your vote and why?

13. Visit a laboratory that has an infrared spectrophotometer. If possible, obtain a spectrogram of a common substance. Explain how to operate the instrument.

14. Look up and describe one of the following:
a. Atomic absorption analysis
b. Colorimetric analysis
c. pH titration
d. Coulometric titration
e. Conductometric titration

15. Are drug companies justified in collaborating on the prices of drugs?

9

AGRICULTURAL CHEMICALS

New and wonderful drugs are not a pure blessing, for there is a serious problem which is aggravated by the successes of the drug developers. The population explosion is producing about 200,000 births a day. We are becoming successful in keeping these people alive as well as extending their life spans. Thanks largely to chemical discoveries, proportionately more of these people will survive infancy than in the past. However, are we keeping the world's population alive so that they can starve to death? About 85 percent of new births are taking place in underdeveloped nations and about 4 million people die of starvation each year. Although many feel that birth control is the answer to mass starvation, there are obstacles to the widespread acceptance of this program, and it still is imperative for the world to provide more food. An added problem is that, as the number of people increases, the amount of farmland decreases. Thus we must provide higher yields of food crops and animals. Also, drastic steps must be taken to protect and expand our supplies of usable water for the future. Chapter 13 will consider this topic in more detail.

Here we want to talk about the research, development, application, and regulation of the chemicals used to assist the farmer in producing more abundant and healthier crops. Without our present insect killers (insecticides), weed killers (herbicides), bacteria killers (bactericides), fungus killers (fungicides), virus killers (virucides), plant growth regulators, and other crop protectors, the supply of crops might drop off in a few years to perhaps one-half what it is today. However, keep in mind that there are still high losses due to insects and diseases that we cannot presently control.

A company that is successfully involved in the development of agricultural chemicals is a wonderful example of scientific teamwork. The synthesis, the production of new compounds, the reactions, the analyses, and the general laboratory study of the chemicals involved are the problems of the research chemists. The insects and diseases that these chemicals combat are studied by entomologists (scientists who study insects), botanists, plant pathologists, plant physiologists, and many other skilled biological experts. The application of the materials on test farms involves agricultural engineers, agronomists (scientists who study the use of land for producing food), soil specialists, and probably most important of all, experienced farmers. The required toxicity testing of the chemicals and the treated crops call for zoologists, microbiologists, pathologists, and medical doctors. Throughout the entire procedure from lab to salable product, of course, there must be able and efficient management to keep all hands working together, to cooperate with the government regulatory agencies, and to provide required data of all sorts so that the product may eventually be approved for consumer use.

SEARCH FOR EFFECTIVE AGENTS

Let us see how a successful agricultural chemical is produced. We shall first recognize that only very large companies are involved in this field, because the cost of developing an agricultural chemical is about $2 to $3 million. It is not too likely that a small outfit could withstand this expense, particularly because after the "gamble" of such an investment is taken, final government approval for use may not be forthcoming. Yet a smaller company may discover a promising structure which it might want to sell to a larger company for development. This sort of dealing goes on in various chemical fields. For instance, recently a company involved essentially in cosmetics discovered a new form of aspirin. After spending considerable time and money to get this product on the market, the company still had not received government approval and consequently sold the product with all rights to a large drug company. Presumably, the drug company, with its greater assets and experience in this field, may be able to market the product.

Getting back to our agricultural chemical research, we find that the large company probably has other divisions in addition to its agricultural one. The agricultural division has complete responsibility for the synthesis of new compounds of possible merit. However, structures that are developed in other divisions and might show chemical activity are tested by the agricultural division.

In addition, some companies solicit new and unusual compounds from schools that are conducting research. I should say that many companies will have nothing to do with many of the larger universities that have become very patent-conscious. It used to be that schools allowed research chemists to deal directly with industrial companies, but now many university administrators frequently ask that the school be named on any patent arising from campus research. Be that as it may, the testing department within the agricultural division is anxious to test any compounds supplied to them.

You may well wonder how a chemist decides upon a structure or series of structures. What is needed to kill a particular worm, destroy a bacterial disease, or combat a fungous infection? We are speaking now of highly complicated biological systems, wherein our knowledge of the mechanisms and their functioning is very vague. We know that the combinations and arrangements of atoms and molecules in the chemical structures are extremely specific. If a chlorine atom were moved from one portion of a molecule to another or if an arrangement of atoms were twisted clockwise rather than counterclockwise, the activity of the compound might disappear or a beneficial effect might even turn into a deadly one. Very little is known about how plant growth regulators, herbicides, and the like operate. Certain types of structures are known to have activity, and hence many related structures are synthesized and tested as a more or less hit-or-miss endeavor. Until much more fundamental knowledge is gained about plant cells, their structure, and their operation, this type of research will continue.

The types of structures studied are usually restricted to fairly uncomplicated ones that can be produced economically. An effective product that the farmer could not afford would be interesting but not useful. Various compounds are therefore sent to the testing laboratory, with a large company screening perhaps 1 or 2 thousand a year. Initial screening for general bactericidal activity can be accomplished by culture testing in an ordinary laboratory. Thereafter, promising plant chemicals are tested on living plants. Large, carefully controlled greenhouses and growth chambers are needed for this purpose. Many plants are available for testing: cotton, beans, tomatoes, grasses, and various weeds. The compounds submitted for screening are usually dissolved or suspended in water at one or two concentrations and sprayed on the test plants. Sometimes a product is sprayed on the earth in which infected seeds are planted (preemergence treatment). The test plants are usually infected after treatment with the test product, although some are infected beforehand.

In walking through a greenhouse, you would probably see a number of pots in which healthy grasses were growing intermingled with various healthy weeds. In one or two pots, you might also observe the grasses to be wilted and discolored due to the application of the test chemical, which will then probably be rejected. So goes the daily search for a good herbicide. Moving along to another bench, you see a group of pots covered with screening. The screening keeps the bugs in contact with the test plants. An effective insecticide does not damage the plant but does kill the test bugs and prevent them from eating or otherwise destroying the plants. Favorable or unfavorable results can be easily seen.

Plant growth regulators are chemicals which affect the growth of plants in a useful way. There are two chief mechanisms involved in plant growth: cell reproduction and cell growth. If the energy expended in growing longer stems could be redirected into more flowering and hence additional fruit, we would be ahead of the game. This is indeed possible with plant growth regulators. A series of test samples might be a number of pots of chrysanthemums. It has been observed that some regulators, when sprayed on a chrysanthemum plant, will kill the top bud without damaging the rest of the plant. This allows branching with a resultant shorter, less stalky plant with many more blossoms.

Certain fungi infect the seeds of plants and pervade the entire plant as it grows. For instance, rust and smut affect barley, wheat, oats, and rye. A systemic fungicide is needed, a chemical which will inhabit the plant and combat the disease throughout. Infected oats in their pots are sprayed with the test products. The results of the tests are easily interpreted since the uncontrolled disease produces withered blossoms and dark spotted areas.

Continuing through the greenhouse, we witness various other tests involving beetles, cotton plants, tomato plants, etc. Chemicals as potential virucides, insecticides, plant growth regulators, and nematocides (to kill tiny worms called nematodes) are sought daily. Out of, say, 2,000 chemicals screened per year, perhaps 200 will be selected for continued screening. Out of this group, perhaps 20 will show enough promise to be tested in company-controlled farmlands. A period of 2 to 3 years has probably now expired, and, with good luck, 5 of the 20 may warrant widespread testing throughout the United States. For this purpose, the company must gain the cooperation of many independent farmers. Finally, one compound may prove to be effective enough under all sorts of conditions and may be safe enough to be put on the open market. The whole process from research lab to sale of product takes about 4 to 5 years and about $2 to $3 million.

APPLICATIONS OF AGRICULTURAL CHEMICALS

I would like to discuss the applications of some of the recent agricultural chemicals. A serious disease called loose smut reduces yields of wheat and barley by as much as 30 percent. One new systemic fungicide appears to control this disease completely. This represents tremendous savings to the wheat and barley growers and a corresponding increase in world food supply. Growth regulators have some interesting effects. For example, in apple orchards many thousands of dollars are lost by apples falling off before they can be picked. Certain regulators can slow down the ripening process and actually make the apples cling better to the limbs until harvest time. Bean plants treated with a plant growth regulator produce less stem and hence more fruit. Similarly, cotton

FIGURE 9–1   BARLEY GROWN FROM UNTREATED AND TREATED SEEDS. THE
ARROWS MARK HEADS RAVAGED BY LOOSE SMUT. (*BY PERMIS-
SION OF UNIROYAL, INC.*)

fields can produce twice as much cotton when the plants are treated
with a regulator. Regulators are used to slow down the growth of grass,
particularly on the sides and median strips of highways. Cutting the
grass less frequently represents a large saving in labor. The homeowner
who hates to cut grass, as I do, should look into this. Trees that interfere
with utility lines and have to be pruned regularly can be treated with a
regulator to slow down their growth.

POSSIBLE HAZARDS

While I have been describing the testing, the development, and the
striking possibilities of agricultural chemicals, I have not discussed the

possible hazards of the various products and the safeguards that the United States government has developed for public protection. Any chemical applied to an edible product can find its way into the human body. Food crops that we use directly will probably contain residual amounts of pesticides (I use this term to refer to all agricultural chemicals that combat insects or diseases) or plant growth regulators. Grass

FIGURE 9–2   THIS FERN HAS ABSORBED RADIOACTIVE SULFUR-35 ALONG WITH THE ORDINARY SULFUR IN ITS FOOD. THE RADIATION GIVEN OFF WAS USED TO MAKE THE PHOTOGRAPH. (BY PERMISSION OF BROOKHAVEN NATIONAL LABORATORY.)

and weeds that are treated may be eaten by animals. In consuming the meat or milk of these animals, we may receive some residual amounts of the chemicals or perhaps some degradation products of the chemicals. Some people have an unreasonable fear of any chemicals and are apprehensive about eating anything that may not be produced in a "natural" way. After all, all living things, including ourselves, are made up of chemicals, some simple and some very complicated. We owe the conquering of some horrible diseases and bodily disorders to the application of certain chemicals; therefore, we should not scorn their value or fear their use. We have observed how very valuable chemicals are in combating food-crop diseases and pests and thus in helping to feed the world. Furthermore, we should realize that a chemical acts in various ways depending upon how much of it is used in a particular situation. It would be no exaggeration to say that almost any material in too great a dosage is toxic.

When an agricultural product is about ready for field testing, the company must contact the Department of Agriculture and the FDA. The company must present all sorts of toxicity data obtained from the testing of the material on animals such as rats and rabbits. Crops treated with the product must be tested for residual concentration, and extensive laboratory testing is performed to see whether the product will break down or change into some hazardous structure. The burden of proving that the product is safe rests completely with the manufacturer. The FDA, which has available a large volume of toxicological data, will, after examining all the data presented by the company, decide whether to approve or disapprove the product. A tolerance limit or maximum residue in the crops involved will be set by the FDA. However, if the structure or any possible degradation of that structure is shown to be cancer-producing (carcinogenic) in man or animal, the chemical will be given a *zero tolerance*. This means that theoretically the food product must not contain even one molecule of the chemical involved. You can appreciate the difficulty of enforcement in such cases. The establishment of a zero tolerance limit can create a difficult analytical problem. The methods of analysis for certain structures may not be sensitive enough to determine whether or not there is a very slight trace present.

The Food, Drug and Cosmetic Act of 1938 is continually being amended. The public needs and deserves protection from a producer who perhaps might wish to overlook or misinterpret certain data in an attempt to show profit. On the other hand, the public should try to be aware of significant scientific advances and allow legitimate chemical industries enough freedom to develop and produce chemicals that will be of value to the whole world.

THE CRANBERRY AFFAIR

Before we leave the topic of agricultural chemicals, I would like to relate an instance in which the FDA stood alone in its effort to protect the public. You no doubt remember the "Cranberry Affair" of 1959. Approval to use a weed killer called aminotriazole had been granted by the Department of Agriculture. This approval had nothing to do with the safety of the product in the consumed cranberries. It only meant that the product was recognized as an effective weed killer. The FDA, knowing that animal tests with aminotriazole showed the formation of malignant tumors, refused to grant a tolerance limit in cranberry products. The product, if applied in the cranberry bogs within a few days after harvest, would not find its way into next year's cranberries. However, application during the growing season would result in aminotriazole being incorporated into the berries. In 1957, the FDA condemned some shipments found contaminated; finally, in 1959 a shipment which represented about 10 percent of the cranberry supply was condemned. Although most of the producers used the agent correctly and hence had untainted berries, good shipments were mixed with bad, with the result that no one could sell any cranberry products and the United States suffered through a Thanksgiving without cranberry sauce. In so protecting the consumer, the Secretary of the Department of Health, Education and Welfare, of which FDA is a part, showed considerable courage, for tremendous commercial and political pressure was brought to bear on him. However, the consumer ought to develop some ability to protect himself. A minimum of awareness will allow the average person to judge whether a matter of personal concern is being decided on the basis of scientific knowledge or political maneuvering. In addition, the public should see to it that the regulatory agencies of the government are staffed with the most qualified personnel in sufficient numbers and with enough equipment and supplies to complete the constantly expanding tasks that lie before them.

QUESTIONS AND PROJECTS

1. Describe the steps taken to produce a pesticide.

2. What are the respective roles of the U.S. Department of Agriculture and the FDA in supervising the development and use of a pesticide?

3. State several useful applications of plant growth regulators.

4. In a biology text look up the relationship between indole-3-acetic acid (IAA) and growth of plants. Suggest a method for testing suspected growth regulators.

5. An effective insecticide is DDT. This chemical is also very persistent, that is, it remains in water or on vegetation for a long time without decomposing. Find out whether the DDT level in humans is rising and whether there is any possible hazard.

6. Report on a visit to an agricultural chemical company or on the film that you watched.

7. Find out how the structures of cellulose and starch differ and relate this to the properties of each.

8. List the trade names, active ingredients, prices, and labeled warnings for 10 household or commercial pesticide products.

9. Determine the number of tons of agricultural chemicals produced in the United States.
a. Last year
b. Five years ago
c. Ten years ago

10. Determine the population of the world
a. Last year
b. Five years ago
c. Ten years ago
Do you feel that the production of agricultural chemicals will ensure sufficient food for the future population?

11. What types of scientific personnel are required in pesticide research?

12. Do you feel that the potential toxicity of pesticides is sufficient reason for complete abandonment of agricultural chemicals? Discuss.

13. What is meant by "zero tolerance"? In what cases is it established? Why is this level an analytical problem?

14. Report on the outcome of the cranberry affair. Did all the berry farmers suffer economic loss? Did the federal government have to pay some of them for their loss?

15. Do you feel that the Department of Health, Education and Welfare should be very strict or very lenient in its treatment of food producers? Explain.

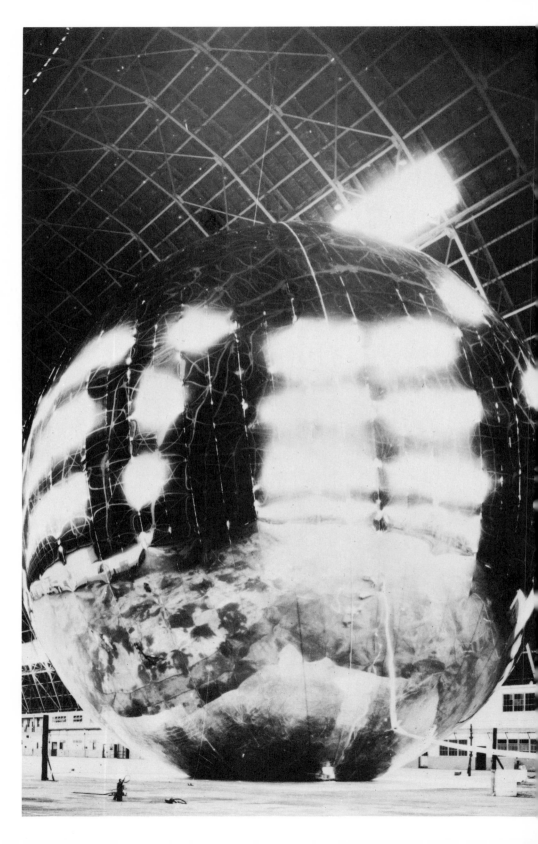

10

POLYMERS I

We have seen how chemical research plays a role in medicine and agriculture. But if someone were asked to name a common application of chemistry in the world about us, he would probably answer, "plastics." The manufacture of useful objects from plastic materials is an industry that is only 30 or 40 years old, and yet the number and variety of plastic products is unbelievable. Anyone can give at least a dozen common examples: synthetic fibers and cloth (nylon, Dacron, etc.); food wraps (polyvinyl acetate and polyvinyl chloride); synthetic rubber (Isoprene); emulsion paints (rubber-base, butadiene-styrene, and acrylic); unbreakable bottles (polyethylene and polypropylene); plastic boats (fiber glass reinforced with a polyester); advertising signs of various shapes and colors (polyacrylates); toys; clocks; radios; auto parts; electrical plugs; flexible and rigid tubing; varnishes; and so forth to infinity. If one stops to consider how many useful and superior products we have available today as compared to a couple of generations ago, we will have to admit that chemistry has indeed produced "better living." In examples of plastic products I have used several long, forbidding names. As in many special fields the nomenclature is the most difficult thing to surmount. Actually, plastics chemistry, or polymer chemistry as we call it, is really a very logical and orderly branch of chemistry. I will give you a brief introduction to the general field and then while examining specific applications we will see how the raw plastics are made, how they are fabricated into end products, and also how the research chemist searches for improved or special plastic materials.

Poly means many, and *meros* means part; so in calling plastics polymers, we are already saying something about their nature. We can get a better picture by thinking of a children's building set—the kind that consists of a number of metal or wood girders. These can be connected at the ends to make any kind of building or object. Let's consider a single girder to be a chemical compound called a *monomer* (literally, a "one-part"). Now we connect another girder to the first in a straight line. Two monomers attached are called a dimer, three a trimer, etc. We will see now that single units (monomers) can be connected and arranged in various patterns to make up polymers. We continue to attach girders end to end until we have a very long line. Let us now make several more such lines of girders (called chains), and lay them side by side. Building sets are fabricated so that girders can be connected not only end to end but also at right angles. Here and there between the rows, we place interconnecting girders. The chains are now cross-linked and cannot pull apart. However, they can slide a little back and forth and therefore have some "flexibility." Suppose we continue to make chains of girders, but now instead of placing them on the floor with the others, suppose we hold them above the others by supporting them with vertical interconnecting girders. We then have what looks like the framework of, say, an office building under construction. If we place many more interconnecting girders, of course, we lose our flexibility and gain strength and rigidity.

Just such arrangements occur in the formation of polymers, and two large classes of polymers become evident from our building game. Polymers that consist of straight chains or interconnected straight chains are called *thermoplastic*. Polymers that are three-dimensional and thoroughly interconnected, like the office building framework, are called *thermosetting*. A polymer that is thermoplastic can be heated and melted without being destroyed. On cooling, it comes back to its original condition. Once a polymer that is thermoset has been formed, it cannot be melted without being destroyed. Thus, a thermoplastic polymer can

FIGURE 10–1   ELABORATE SHAPING IS POSSIBLE WITH THERMOPLASTICS, AS IN THIS PIECE OF JEWELRY. (*BY PERMISSION OF MUSEUM OF CONTEMPORARY CRAFTS, NEW YORK, N.Y.*)

be melted and converted into various shapes. This is not true of the thermosetting polymers.

Going back to the erector set, we can see the reason for this difference in properties. The straight chains can move back and forth and pivot and turn. The links interconnecting the chains could be easily removed (as during heating) to give great flexibility and fluidity; and, finally, the links could be replaced (as in cooling) to return to the original solid condition. This is the thermoplastic class. On the other hand, a highly interconnected three-dimensional structure, which is very rigid, would not be affected except by very high temperatures, whereupon irreversible decomposition would take place. Such a structure belongs to the thermosetting class.

ETHYLENE TO POLYETHYLENE

If we replace the girders with chemical building blocks or monomers, we can prepare various thermoplastic and thermosetting polymers. A common thermoplastic is polyethylene. We use a great deal of polyethylene for plastic wrapping, wire coatings, bottles, and containers. As the name suggests, polyethylene is made up of many units of ethylene.

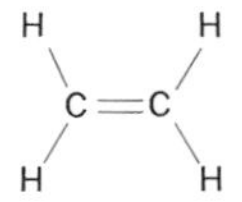

Ethylene

Each line represents a pair of electrons that are being shared between atoms. The double line between the two carbons indicates that two pairs of electrons are being shared to form a *double covalent bond.* In the diagrammatic formula of the molecule the two bonds between the carbon atoms appear to be equivalent, but this is not the case. One of the bonds results from a direct "head-on" overlapping of orbitals, called a *sigma bond,* while the other bond results from a sideways overlapping of orbitals which are at right angles to the other orbitals. I'll try to make that a little clearer. Consider that the two carbon atoms and four hydrogen atoms are on a tabletop in the arrangement shown in the diagram. (Fig. 10–2). One of the bonds in the double bond involves overlapping of orbitals that are in between the two carbon atoms. Now picture for each carbon atom a *p* orbital extending above and below the surface of the table. These orbitals overlap in a sideways action. This *pi bond* (labeled π, the Greek letter pi) is not as strong as the sigma bond (labeled σ) and can be broken more easily. Under the proper conditions, then, the ethylene monomer can break the π portion of the double bond,

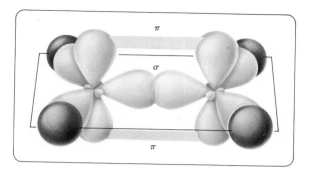

FIGURE 10–2   ETHYLENE.

and carbon atoms from adjacent molecules have an opportunity to attach to each other.

$$-\underset{\underset{H}{|}}{\overset{\overset{H}{|}}{C}}-\underset{\underset{H}{|}}{\overset{\overset{H}{|}}{C}}-\underset{\underset{H}{|}}{\overset{\overset{H}{|}}{C}}-\underset{\underset{H}{|}}{\overset{\overset{H}{|}}{C}}-\text{etc.}$$

Chains of various lengths and hence various molecular weights (i.e., the combined weights of all the atoms in a chain) are obtainable by varying the conditions of the reaction. For instance, amount of reactants, temperature, pressure, and heating time can all be varied.

Polymers that are employed in useful end products are usually mixed with other ingredients which impart special properties. We refer to the basic polymer as the resin. The remainder of this chapter will be devoted to the thermosetting resins, leaving the thermoplastics for the following chapter.

THERMOSETTING POLYMERS

PHENOL FORMALDEHYDE CLASS

An example of a thermosetting resin is the class called *phenol formaldehydes*. The familiar Bakelite is a member of this class. Remember that the thermosetting plastics are like the office building framework: the monomers are highly interconnected. With such monomers as ethylene, which can only "connect" in two positions, we can only achieve an end-to-end or chain structure. However, if we use a monomer that can react in more than two positions we can attain cross-linking and a resultant rigid configuration. Phenol, C_6H_5OH, sometimes called carbolic acid, can be represented as follows: →P←. The arrows indicate the three sites of reactivity. Formaldehyde, CH_2O, can be made to react with phenol by simple heating. At each reactive site of the phenol molecules a hydrogen atom is released. These hydrogen atoms combine with the oxygen in the formaldehyde to form water, H_2O. The carbon atom in the formaldehyde bonds onto the reactive sites formerly occupied by the hydrogen atoms.

Figure 10–3 shows, in two dimensions only, the beginning of the interconnecting process which can lead to a giant structure that will not flow with the application of heat. Please note that this polymerization involves the elimination of water, whereas the polyethylene polymerization merely added one unit to another. The former, wherein a small molecule, usually water, is eliminated, is called *condensation polymerization* and the latter *addition polymerization*.

For such a resin to be useful in the manufacture of end products, the polymerization reaction must not be allowed to go to completion. The resin producer stops the reaction at an intermediate stage and sells this material in the form of pellets or powder (often called molding compound). The fabricator of a plastic article can make this material into the desired form and complete the polymerization reaction, usually with pressure and heat. The intermediate stage is commonly referred to

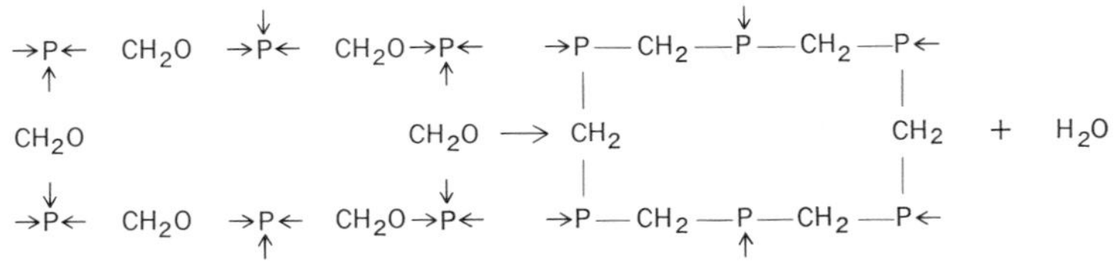

$$\rightarrow \overset{\uparrow}{P}\leftarrow \quad CH_2O \quad \rightarrow \overset{\downarrow}{\underset{\uparrow}{P}}\leftarrow \quad CH_2O \rightarrow \overset{}{\underset{\uparrow}{P}}\leftarrow \quad \rightarrow P \!-\! CH_2 \!-\! \overset{\downarrow}{P} \!-\! CH_2 \!-\! P\leftarrow$$

$$CH_2O \qquad\qquad\qquad CH_2O \rightarrow CH_2 \qquad\qquad CH_2 \quad + \quad H_2O$$

$$\rightarrow \overset{\downarrow}{P}\leftarrow \quad CH_2O \quad \rightarrow \overset{}{\underset{\uparrow}{P}}\leftarrow \quad CH_2O \rightarrow \overset{\downarrow}{P}\leftarrow \quad \rightarrow P \!-\! CH_2 \!-\! \underset{\uparrow}{P} \!-\! CH_2 \!-\! P\leftarrow$$

FIGURE 10–3

as a *B* stage, while the monomer is the *A* stage and the fully polymerized (or "cured") resin is the *C* stage.

The phenol formaldehyde class has a large number of uses. The molding powders or pellets are mixed with various fillers to give special properties. For instance, mica can be added for electrical resistance, while chopped fabric is used for shock resistance. Telephone headsets, steering wheels, and electrical switches are a few other uses. Liquid resins are used commonly in plywood and other laminated board construction. They impart strength and act as adhesives as well. All sorts of foamed plastics (plastics which are "puffed up" and have a honeycomb or cellular structure) are finding very wide application. Foamed phenol formaldehyde resins are being used for such things as insulation and packaging.

POLYESTERS

This class finds application in the Dacron fabrics, in fiberglass boats and auto bodies, and in the familiar alkyd paints.

A table setting often includes a bottle of vinegar. We know this to be a sour substance which improves the taste of many foods. The sour ingredient is an acid known as acetic acid. The chemist represents the structure as $CH_3—\overset{\displaystyle O}{\overset{\|}{C}}—OH$. The $—\overset{\displaystyle O}{\overset{\|}{C}}—OH$ grouping is a *functional* group characteristic of a large family of carbon-containing *acids*. Also found on many tables is a cocktail, a bottle of wine, or a glass of beer. Their common ingredient, of course, is alcohol—specifically ethyl alcohol. The formula for this is $CH_3—CH_2—OH$. The functional group here is the hydroxyl group, the $—OH$ portion, while the other portion is called the ethyl group. As pointed out in Chap. 5, there is a whole family of alcohols. If we exchange the ethyl group for a methyl group, we have methyl alcohol ($CH_3—OH$). This is known as wood alcohol and has often been consumed accidentally, causing blindness and death. Isopropyl alcohol, $[CH_3]_2CH—OH$, well known as rubbing alcohol, is also poisonous. We may represent the family of alcohols as $R—OH$, and similarly we may represent the family of acids as $R—\overset{\displaystyle O}{\overset{\|}{C}}—OH$.

If we react an acid such as acetic acid with an alcohol such as ethyl alcohol, we obtain a product the chemists refer to as an *ester*. In the following diagram the ethyl alcohol molecule is turned around so that its reaction with the acid will be clear:

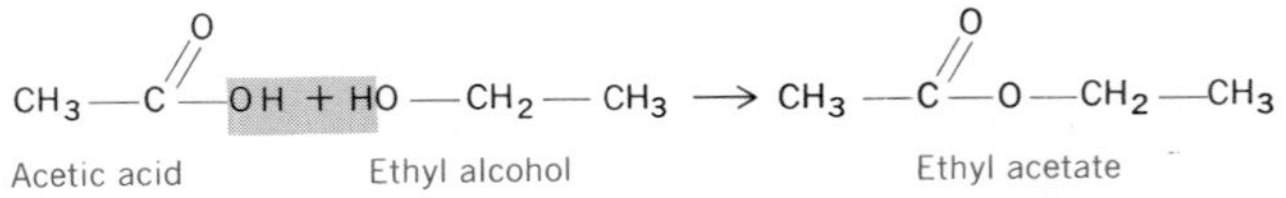

$$CH_3-C\overset{O}{\diagup}OH + HO-CH_2-CH_3 \longrightarrow CH_3-C\overset{O}{\diagup}O-CH_2-CH_3$$

  Acetic acid   Ethyl alcohol   Ethyl acetate

The product in this example is ethyl acetate, and the general reaction is called *esterification*. A general formula for the ester class is $R-\overset{O}{\underset{||}{C}}-O-R$. If we use a monomer acid with two acid functional groups, one at each end of the monomer, and if we add a monomer alcohol with two alcohol functional groups, one at each end, we could get a long chain polymer similar to polyethylene. In view of this straight chain structure, you should question whether this polymer belongs in this chapter on the thermosetting class or in the next chapter. You are quite right in feeling that this particular type of polyester is thermoplastic. An important example of this type of polyester is Dacron, well known to all of us. However, if we use alcohols that have more than two functional groups or if we use acids containing double bonds, we do obtain thermosetting polyester resins. With alcohols that have, say, three functional groups, esterification can take place in three dimensions and can thus yield a highly cross-linked structure. Alternately, by use of an acid with a double bond in its structure, one can produce polyester chains with double bonds. This condition is called *unsaturation*. Now if another monomer containing a double bond (such as styrene $C_6H_5-CH=CH_2$) is added to the resin, cross-linking can take place between chains, through the monomer, in much the same manner as the polymerization of polyethylene.

The below diagram shows how two polyester chains can be interconnected through double bond polymerization.

We are all familiar with "alkyd" paints. Alkyd, a blend of the two words alcohol and acid, is often used in place of the term polyester. Almost all enamel or gloss paints are based on alkyd resins. Polyesters are used to a great extent to reinforce fiber glass in boat construction, in fishing rods, and in household articles. The resins owe their wide

$$
\begin{array}{ccc}
\text{Chain}-\overset{\text{H}}{\underset{\text{H}}{\text{C}}}\!=\!\text{C}-\text{Chain} & & \text{Chain}-\overset{\text{H}}{\text{C}}-\overset{\uparrow\ \text{Next chain}}{\text{C}}-\text{Chain}
\end{array}
$$

application to their strength, their electrical and insulating properties, and their resistance to solvents, sun, and salt water.

EPOXY RESINS

When one needs a plastic which is very tough, is a good electrical insulator over a wide temperature range, and is resistant to chemicals and solvents, an *epoxy* resin is probably the answer. Epoxy resins are thermosetting resins made from epichlorohydrin and a large alcohol with two alcohol functional groups. Epichlorohydrin has the structure $CH_2\!-\!CH\!-\!CH_2\!-\!Cl$. The term *epoxy* means "oxygen upon." The oxygen atom appears to be perched upon the two carbon atoms. The resins made from epichlorohydrin have consequently been referred to as epoxy. When a hydroxyl group —OH reacts with the epoxy end of the molecule, the following takes place (*R* represents the rest of the molecule):

$$
R-OH\ +\ CH_2\!-\!CH\!-\!CH_2\!-\!Cl\ \longrightarrow\ R-OH\ +\ CH_2\!-\!CH\!-\!CH_2\!-\!Cl\ \longrightarrow
$$

An alcohol   Epichlorohydrin

$$
R-O-CH_2\!-\!CH\!-\!CH_2\!-\!Cl
$$

The hydrogen atom from the hydroxyl group attaches itself to the epoxy oxygen atom, and the hydroxyl oxygen atom attaches to the terminal carbon atom. Note that a new hydroxyl group is created. At the other end of the epichlorohydrin, another reaction can take place, as follows:

$$
CH_2\!-\!CH\!-\!CH_2\!-\!Cl\ +\ HO-R\ \longrightarrow\ CH_2\!-\!CH\!-\!CH_2\!-\!O-R\ +\ HCl
$$

A molecule of hydrogen chloride is eliminated. Let us now look at both reactions together:

$$
\begin{array}{l}
\text{HO} - \text{R} - \text{OH} \ + \ \overset{\displaystyle O}{\overset{\displaystyle \triangle}{\text{CH}_2 - \text{CH}}} - \text{CH} - \text{Cl} \ + \ \text{HO} - \text{R} - \text{OH} \ \longrightarrow \\[2em]
\qquad\qquad\qquad\quad \overset{\displaystyle \text{OH}}{\overset{\displaystyle |}{}} \\[0.5em]
\text{HO} - \text{R} - \text{O} - \text{CH}_2 - \text{CH} - \text{CH} - \text{O} - \text{R} - \text{OH} \ + \ \text{HCl}
\end{array}
$$

You can see how long chains can be built up. These chains with reactive hydroxyl groups now undergo cross-linking by the same sort of reactions that produced the chains.

Epoxies make good electrical components, especially where metal parts need to be embedded. They are used as insulators, adhesives for metal and wood, and surface coatings for floors, tanks, and beer cans.

POLYURETHANES

The *polyurethanes* have become a very well-known class of polymers, particularly in foam applications for furniture, automobile safety padding, life preservers, and carpeting. A urethane is made from an alcohol and an isocyanate. The latter has the structure $R - N = C = O$, and the alcohol, we know, is a hydroxyl compound, $B - OH$. The reaction can be represented as follows:

$$
\text{R} - \text{N} = \text{C} = \text{O} \ + \ \text{HO} - \text{B} \ \longrightarrow \ \text{R} - \text{N} - \text{C} = \text{O} \ + \ \text{HO} - \text{B} \ \longrightarrow \ \text{R} - \text{N} - \overset{\displaystyle O}{\overset{\displaystyle \parallel}{\text{C}}} - \text{O} - \text{B}
$$

| Isocyanate | Alcohol | | | Urethane |

Now, just as with the polyester class, if we have a monomer with two isocyanate functional groups and an alcohol with two hydroxyl functional groups, we can obtain a long chain. These resins have elastic properties and show some advantages as a synthetic rubber. If we use an alcohol with more than two functional groups, we get cross-linking and a resul-

FIGURE 10–4   THERMOSETTING SITTING. *(BY PERMISSION OF MUSEUM OF CONTEMPORARY CRAFTS, NEW YORK, N.Y.)*

tant rigid, three-dimensional structure. If water is added to an isocyanate, carbon dioxide gas, CO_2, is liberated. During the formation of a polyurethane, advantage is taken of this reaction. Some water is added, gas is liberated, and the plastic puffs up and becomes a foam. Freons (gaseous fluorocarbons) are familiar to us as propellants in household spray products. Freons can be used in place of water to produce the foaming effect. Varying the amount of water or Freon and the type of alcohol and isocyanate results in foams with varying properties. These are generally classified as flexible or rigid. For safety padding, furniture, and bedding, where flexible foams are needed, the flexible foam plastics are replacing many of the familiar foam rubber products. For insulation in the construction industry, aircraft, and refrigerators, rigid foams are employed. New and unique applications for this relatively new field of polymers are being sought by many large chemical manufacturers.

QUESTIONS AND PROJECTS

1. Make a foam ball model of the ethylene molecule.

2. Explain the difference between a sigma bond and a pi bond.

3. Compare the structures and properties of thermosetting and thermoplastic resins.

4. How are foam polyurethanes produced? Name four applications.

5. To which class of plastic does the trade name Bakelite apply?

6. Find the names of and write the structures for the starting materials for Dacron.

7. Look up the names of three other polyester resins and give their properties.

8. Draw a two-dimensional structure for an epoxy resin. Using at least two molecules of epichlorohydrin for each chain, make four parallel chains. Show how the chains can be interconnected.

9. List specific applications for the various thermosetting resins.

10. Using a monomer containing two isocyanate groups and a monomer containing two alcohol groups, draw the structure for the resulting polymer chain. Show how a three-dimensional structure could be obtained by increasing the number of functioning groups.

11. Acetylene has the following structure:
$H-C \equiv C-H$
Each carbon atom has two sp hybrid bonds and two p orbitals each at right angles to each other and the sp bonds. The p orbitals overlap sideways, yielding two pi bonds. Make a foam ball model of acetylene.

12. Make foam ball models of a dimer, a trimer, and a tetramer of ethylene.

13. Write equations for the formation of methylacetate and ethyl acetate.

14. Write formulas for
a. Formaldehyde
b. Ethylene
c. Acetic acid
d. Methyl alcohol
e. An acid with three —COOH groups

15. Do you suppose that eyeglass frames are made of thermosetting or thermoplastic resins? Why?

11

POLYMERS II

We have been introduced to the field of polymers and have examined the class of resins called thermosetting. In this chapter, we will study the thermoplastic resins which can be melted and shaped, and then, on cooling, can be returned to their original state.

In our discussion of the difference between the two classes, we recall that thermoplastic resins consisted of long chains rather than of a highly interconnected three-dimensional system. Let us take a closer look at these straight-chain fellows. Some have low softening points, some have high. Some are tough and rigid, others are soft and flexible. What decides these properties are length of chains and attraction between molecules. Generally, low molecular weight (that is, short chains) gives a lower softening point, and high molecular weight (long chains) gives a higher one. As for intermolecular attraction, I can best introduce you to that subject by considering some simple molecules. Back in Chap. 4, when we were talking about bonding, we said that the hydrogen atom, the simplest atom, consists of a proton and an electron. This electron is in the $1s$ orbital, the only orbital in the first major shell of electrons.

Recall that each orbital can hold a maximum of two electrons, and accordingly, the first major shell can hold no more than two electrons. Helium, the next larger element, has this first shell completed and is a relatively inert atom. A hydrogen atom, you will recall, attains this completed shell configuration by overlapping its 1s orbital with the 1s orbital of an adjacent hydrogen atom. The structure then for hydrogen gas is H—H. The two electrons are being shared evenly between the two protons. Remember that the proton has a positive charge and the electron a negative charge. Since both protons are identical, the two-electron cloud is now smeared evenly about the two protons. Neither proton is getting a better share of the two electrons, and hence one end of the molecule is no more negative or positive than the other end. We call this a *nonpolar molecule.* H—H is a special case in that both atoms in the molecule are the same element. Most bonds, however, involve different atoms.

Let's look at a molecule such as hydrogen chloride, H—Cl. First, try to recall our earlier discussion of the electronic structure of the atoms. Atoms that had an almost completed set of s and p orbitals generally would try to complete those orbitals and thus gain the next inert gas structure. On the other hand, atoms that had one or two more electrons than the last previous inert gas structure would tend to lose those electrons and thus gain the previous inert gas configuration. Atoms that gain electrons are called *electronegative,* and those that lose electrons are called *electropositive.*

Now, back to hydrogen chloride. The chlorine atom is more electronegative than hydrogen; hence the sharing of the pair of electrons in the covalent bond between them is uneven. The chlorine atom gets a better hold on that pair of electrons. Remember that before the bond took place the hydrogen atom was neutral, with one proton and one electron. Likewise, the chlorine atom was neutral, with seventeen protons and seventeen electrons. Now each atom provides one electron for the bond between them, but the chlorine "hogs" these two electrons and pulls the pair of them closer to itself. As a result, chlorine, which put up one electron in the deal, gets back more than one-half of two electrons and thus ends up with more negative charge than it started out with. Please note that it did not take the hydrogen's electron away completely. If this were the case, we would not have a covalent bond but an ionic bond. We have a molecule now which is more negative at one end, the chlorine end, than at the other. We call this a *polar molecule*. All of us have played with magnets and recall how the north and south poles will snap together and how similar poles will repel one another. Positive and negative electric charges work the same way in that like charges repel and unlike charges attract. When an H—Cl molecule sneaks up beside another H—Cl molecule, how will the molecules line up? You're right— the chlorine end of one molecule will get close to the hydrogen end of the other. Such intermolecular forces of attraction are very important. Without them, molecules would not want to stick together as they do in solids and liquids, and matter would probably exist in the gaseous state in which molecules have very little attraction for one another. The more polarity a molecule has, then, the better it can stick together with its neighbors. A polar solid is generally crystalline, that is, the molecules are arranged in a definite pattern and are held firmly together. This internal arrangement is responsible for external properties, such as hardness and rigidity.

PHYSICAL CHEMISTRY OF THERMOPLASTICS

By now you are certainly wondering what all this has to do with thermoplastic polymers. Thermoplastics are generally long-chain polymers with relatively weak forces holding the chains together. Thus, on heating, the interchain bonds are broken; on cooling, they are re-formed. Some of these polymers soften easily and some with more difficulty. Making chains that fit together well and that have polarity will result in highly crystalline rigid thermoplastics. On the other hand, polymers composed of chains that cannot get close together and that do not have polarity will be less crystalline or even noncrystalline (called *amorphous*).

The first example in this class that I have given you so far is polyethylene:

$$-\overset{\displaystyle \underset{\displaystyle H}{H}}{\underset{\displaystyle H}{C}}-\overset{\displaystyle \underset{\displaystyle H}{H}}{\underset{\displaystyle H}{C}}-\overset{\displaystyle \underset{\displaystyle H}{H}}{\underset{\displaystyle H}{C}}-\overset{\displaystyle \underset{\displaystyle H}{H}}{\underset{\displaystyle H}{C}}-\text{etc.}$$

Here, since the chains are very regular and can fit together well, we have crystallinity. However, it is not a high degree of crystallinity since the ethylene molecule itself is nonpolar. Carbon and hydrogen have similar electronegativities. On the other hand, nylon, which consists of long chains of carbon and nitrogen atoms, is much more crystalline. Its crystallinity provides the important property of strength so characteristic of nylon fiber. This increased crystallinity is due to the fact that the molecules are polar and the chains are effectively attracted to one another. In the molecule, there are nitrogen-hydrogen bonds (nitrogen is much more electronegative than hydrogen) and carbon-oxygen bonds (oxygen is more electronegative than carbon). Sometimes, however, chains are polar but since they have awkward groups of atoms protruding sideways from the chains, they cannot get close enough together to let the polarity take effect. An example of this is polystyrene which consists of long carbon chains, like those of polyethylene, but with large six-membered rings of carbon atoms attached in a helter-skelter fashion all along the chains. No close approach of the chains is possible, and as a result we have an amorphous (noncrystalline) structure with a relatively low softening point.

Let us now examine individual thermoplastic resins. We will start with the familiar polyethylene.

THERMOPLASTIC POLYMERS

POLYETHYLENE

Billions of pounds of these low-cost thermoplastics are being produced each year. They find great application in film, containers, and insulation. The structure of polyethylene has already been presented. Actually, I have cheated a little bit to keep our discussion of the structure of thermoplastics as simple as possible. In fact, two types of polyethylene with two kinds of structures are available. There are high-density and low-density polyethylenes. The high-density grade has the simple straight-chain structure shown above and is prepared in chambers at low pressures with the help of certain chemicals we call *catalysts*. Catalysts are agents that influence reactions, either helping or hindering, but are not consumed in the reaction. These materials, whose action is often not well understood, are very important in research and production. The low-density grade of polyethylene, which is prepared under different conditions, has a lower softening point. This is due to the fact that the resultant product contains side chains sticking out from the main chain.

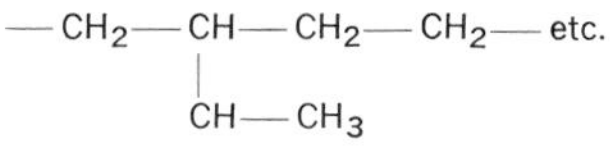

$$-CH_2-CH-CH_2-CH_2- \text{ etc.}$$
$$\quad\quad\;\; |$$
$$\quad\quad CH-CH_3$$

These side chains prevent close approach and result in less crystallinity, a lower softening point, and lower density than the straight-chain polyethylene.

POLYPROPYLENE

Another polymer very similar to polyethylene is *polypropylene.* The monomer has the following structure:

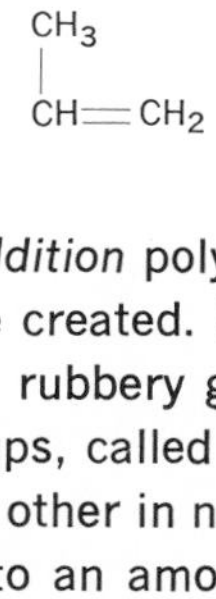

$$CH_3$$
$$|$$
$$CH=CH_2$$

The chains are produced by *addition* polymerization in the same manner that polyethylene polymers are created. However, if this reaction is conducted under high pressure, a rubbery goo or oily liquid results. Under these conditions, the CH_3 groups, called methyl groups, find themselves on one side of the chain or the other in no particular order. This messed-up arrangement corresponds to an amorphous structure. However, the use of special catalysts can control the addition reaction by allowing the monomers to add onto the growing chain only in a certain way. This results in regular chains, wherein the methyl groups are all on one side of the chain or are on alternate sides of the chain. With such regular arrangements, chains can fit together and crystallinity occurs. As a matter of fact, polypropylene has a higher softening point than polyethylene and has somewhat better hardness. Aside from foam plastics, polypropylene is the lightest of all plastics. It is used in packaging films and in tank linings, toys, bottles, and many other applications.

ACRYLICS

This class of thermoplastic polymer is probably best known to us by virtue of such names as Plexiglas and Lucite. The latter are trade names for polymethyl methacrylate, used in great volume for windshields, sky domes, paneling, and outdoor signs. The two most important monomers are methyl acrylate and methyl methacrylate. Note that the two starting materials are the same up to a methyl group, CH_3—, or a hydrogen atom,

$$H—, \text{ and that these belong to the ester class, } R—\overset{\displaystyle O}{\overset{\displaystyle \|}{C}}—OR.$$ (See p. 119.)

As in the case of propylene, polymerization takes place by addition. The double bond "opens up," and adjacent molecules attach onto one another. A variety of products with a corresponding variety of properties can be obtained. The monomers shown above can be polymerized separately, or they can be polymerized together in various proportions, the

FIGURE 11–1   PLEXIGLAS TRIANGLES 8 FEET ON A SIDE MAKE UP THIS PLANE-
TARIUM IN PORTLAND, OREGON. (*BY PERMISSION OF ROHM
AND HAAS COMPANY.*)

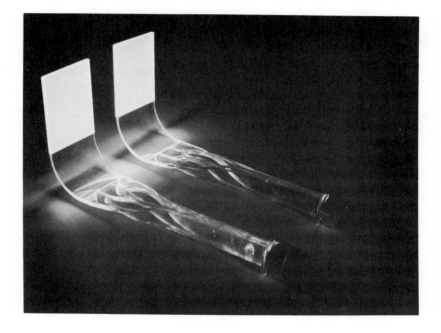

Methyl acrylate   Methyl methacrylate

latter process being called *copolymerization*. Furthermore, the methyl group located on the oxygen atom can be replaced with other larger groups.

The most outstanding properties of the acrylics include excellent optical clarity (comparable to that of glass) and excellent resistance to outdoor

FIGURE 11–2   LIGHT CAN BE "PIPED" AROUND CORNERS WITH LUCITE. HERE, THE LIGHT IS BEING CARRIED FROM THE GLOWING PANELS INTO THE ELECTRONIC DEVICES AT RIGHT. (*BY PERMISSION OF LAWRENCE RADIATION LABORATORY, UNIVERSITY OF CALIFORNIA.*)

conditions. Added to these are such properties as film-forming, adhesion, toughness, and resistance to acids and alkalis. Advantage is taken of these properties in the preparation of cast sheet (large panels that can be fabricated into useful articles such as signs and skylights); lacquers; water-base paints; adhesives and coatings for leather, paper, and textiles (to promote crease resistance); optical lenses; and floor waxes. The particular use of the polymer dictates the method of manufacture of the raw polymer required by the fabricator.

BULK POLYMERIZATION

For example, cast sheet of various sizes, thicknesses, and colors is obtained by the production method called *bulk polymerization.* As the name implies, the monomer is reacted in bulk. Nothing but a catalyst is added to the monomer, with the result that the product is almost completely pure acrylate. For the preparation of polymethyl methacrylate sheets, provision must be made for considerable shrinkage during reaction and for removal of the heat liberated by the reacting molecules. Pigments can be added to produce colored sheeting, if desired.

SOLUTION POLYMERIZATION

Another method of production of thermoplastics is *solution polymerization.* Here polymerization takes place in a solvent that can dissolve both monomer and polymer. The end product is generally used in solution form, for example, as an adhesive or a lacquer. To obtain a pure polymer by this method is generally difficult and expensive. Removal and recovery of a solvent present a number of problems.

EMULSION POLYMERIZATION

A third method commonly used is *emulsion polymerization.* This involves adding the monomer and a special detergent to a large volume of water and stirring to yield an emulsion. (A well-known example of an emulsion is a product of this type of polymerization—water-base paints.) A catalyst which is soluble in water is added, and the reaction commences with the application of heat. Once the reaction begins, heat is liberated from within. However, removal of heat is not as great a problem as it is in bulk polymerization where there is no water or solvent to help absorb the heat. This represents a very distinct advantage for emulsion polymerization. The resultant emulsion can be used as is, or the polymer can be "thrown out" of solution by the addition of certain chemicals. After separation from the water, the product, called a *latex,* is collected. Acrylic emulsions and latexes are used in water-based paints, coatings, and floor waxes.

SUSPENSION POLYMERIZATION

Still another method for production of thermoplastics is *suspension polymerization.* This method, which is similar to the emulsion method, involves the agitation of the monomer in a large amount of water. The monomer is broken up into small particles, and a protective material is added to coat the particles and to prevent their joining together. A catalyst is added which is soluble not in the water but in the monomer. Thus we are really conducting a large number of bulk polymerizations, but in the presence of a lot of water which can conveniently absorb the heat liberated. The result is a product in the form of small beads. In this form, the polymer can be conveniently compressed into various forms of finished products, such as telephones, safety goggles, contact lenses, and artificial eyes.

TEFLON POLYMERS

A woman in the kitchen is very familiar with, and thankful for, Teflon-coated frying pans and cooking utensils. This highly stain-resistant, temperature-resistant, and easily cleanable plastic is indeed a great help in cooking. It has many other applications in less familiar but equally important areas. The starting material is tetrafluoroethane.

Tetrafluoroethane

As in polyethylene, chains are built up by the opening up of the double bond and the addition of one molecule to another. The carbon-fluorine bonds are very strong, and the fluorine atoms are relatively small, with the result that very compact, regular chains result. Adjacent chains can pack together very neatly, and a highly crystalline state results, with corresponding properties of hardness and strength. Fluorinated polymers such as Teflon have unusual chemical resistance and electrical insulating properties. Moreover, they can be effectively employed over a wide range of temperatures. Some applications include gaskets, seals, piston rings, filters, pipe linings, and wire coverings.

POLYVINYLCHLORIDE (PVC)

Probably the most common use of PVC is in film for packaging purposes. Sandwich and meat wrapping that can be heat-sealed is manufactured in enormous quantities. PVC has excellent chemical resistance, weather resistance, and electrical insulating properties. Such qualities allow widespread applications in many fields. The starting material is vinyl chloride.

$$\begin{array}{cc} H & Cl \\ \diagdown & \diagup \\ C = C & \\ \diagup & \diagdown \\ H & H \end{array}$$

Vinyl chloride

This polymerization proceeds in the same fashion as for polyethylene and Teflon. However, the resultant polymer is not a crystalline one. The chlorine atoms in the chains do not arrange themselves in a regular fashion, and their random arrangement (atactic) yields an amorphous condition. However, PVC and PVC copolymers (PVC and polyvinyl acetate) have such outstanding properties that they are among the leaders in the thermoplastics field. Besides packaging applications, PVC is used in plumbing, especially where chemicals are employed, in tank linings, corrugated roofing, phonograph records, cable coatings, and floor tiles. Foamed PVC is being used in carpet liners, upholstery, and mattresses.

POLYSTYRENE

Polystyrene finds wide application in the packaging field. Large quantities of food and household containers are made of this transparent, colorless, and fairly strong thermoplastic. The monomer is styrene, as follows:

$$\begin{array}{c} H \\ \diagdown \\ C = CH_2 \\ \diagup \\ C_6H_5 \end{array}$$

Styrene

The C_6H_5 group is called a phenyl group and consists of a relatively bulky ring of six carbon atoms. The rings, which are in no regular arrangement on the chains, prevent close approach of one chain to another. Hence an atactic polymer results. Polystyrene, accordingly, has a relatively low softening point and not too great an impact strength. However, it does have excellent electrical properties, clarity, and good chemical resistance. It can be prepared by bulk, solvent, emulsion, or suspension polymerization depending upon the final application involved.

POLYSTYRENE MANUFACTURE

Let us take a quick visit to a manufacturer of polystyrene molding compound. This, you will recall, is a resin which may then be converted into finished products. The process employed is the suspension method. Huge covered tanks with jackets for heating or cooling are used for carrying out the reaction. The tanks have a 25,000-gallon capacity and are capable of producing about 10,000 pounds of polystyrene in one batch. Monomer is introduced onto the surface of the water which has already been run into the tank. A catalyst called benzoyl peroxide is dissolved in the monomer, and a water-soluble suspending agent called tricalcium phosphate is added. Stirring by means of large paddles driven by powerful electric motors is begun, and the monomer is "beat up" into tiny droplets. The rate of stirring controls the size of these droplets and hence the size of the resultant resin particles. To get the reaction started, heat is applied by running hot water through the tank jacket. When the temperature rises to about 180°F, the hot water is replaced with cold water to remove the large amount of heat liberated (this is called an *exothermic reaction*—some reactions absorb a net amount of heat and are called *endothermic*). The operator must watch this reaction very carefully. If the pressure gets too high, indicating a "runaway" reaction, he must discharge the mixture to prevent a possible explosion. Some tanks are provided with automatic pressure relief mechanisms; sometimes the mechanisms work and sometimes they do *not*. The resin, which settles to the bottom of the tank in the form of colorless little spheres, is drawn off, washed thoroughly, and dried in a rotary oven similar to a large dryer in a laundromat. In this shape the resin does not lend itself to casting, and it is therefore converted into another form. It is heated up and forced through tiny openings in a metal plate much like a meat grinder. The product is cut off on the other side in shapes resembling short pieces of spaghetti. During this step, called extrusion, pigments and other ingredients can be added to suit the end product requirements.

Polystyrene and various copolymers are used in radio cabinets, taillights, packaging, electrical parts, insulation, wallboard, synthetic rubber (styrene and butadiene), refrigerator parts, and camera cases.

POLYAMIDES (Nylons)

Certainly everyone (at least everyone who wears clothes) is familiar with nylon, the remarkable plastic material which makes possible so many modern fibers and textiles. Recall from the discussion of polyesters that linear polyesters can be made from difunctional acids and difunctional alcohols. Dacron is a useful member of this class of polymers. Polyamides form by a condensation between acids and amines similar to the reaction that takes place between acids and alcohols in polyester formation. An acid, we have seen, has the general structure R—COOH. An amine will require an introduction. Ammonia is a common household cleaning agent with a disagreeable or agreeable odor depending on the reaction of the sniffer. The products are generally water solutions of ammonia. In the pure state, ammonia is actually a gas, the formula for which is NH_3. If we replace one of the hydrogen atoms with a group such as the methyl group, CH_3—, we have methyl amine, CH_3—NH_2, the simplest member of a large family of *amines*.

The NH_2 group is then the functional group for the amine family, which we can represent as R—NH_2. Now let us look at the reaction between an acid and an amine. Note that the amine structure has been turned around for clarity.

$$R—\underset{\text{Acid}}{\overset{\displaystyle\overset{O}{\|}}{C}—OH} \quad \underset{\text{Amine}}{H—\overset{\displaystyle\overset{H}{|}}{N}—R} \longrightarrow R—\underset{\text{Amide}}{\overset{\displaystyle\overset{O}{\|}}{C}—\overset{\displaystyle\overset{H}{|}}{N}—R} + H_2O$$

The resultant structure is called an *amide*. Now if we use a difunctional acid and a difunctional amine, the units can attach at both ends of both molecules, resulting in long chain structures. For instance:

Amine   Acid   Amine

A polyamide, Nylon-66

Please note that we have in the chain structure paired nitrogen and hydrogen atoms and paired carbon and oxygen atoms. Remember our talk about polarity between atoms of differing electronegativity? The nitrogen atoms are more negative than the hydrogens, and the oxygens are more negative than the carbons or the hydrogens. This results in an attraction between chains, as follows:

$$—\overset{\ominus}{N}—$$
$$|$$
$$\overset{\underset{\oplus}{}}{H}$$

$$\overset{\ominus}{\underset{\|}{O}}$$
$$—\overset{}{\underset{\oplus}{C}}—$$

This is a special situation we call *hydrogen bonding.* It occurs wherever a hydrogen atom is attached to a very electronegative element, such as nitrogen or oxygen. Indeed, if it were not for hydrogen bonding in H_2O, water molecules would not be held so tightly together, and water would probably be a gas at ordinary temperatures—what a problem that would be!

Back to the nylon structure. The chains can pack closely together, and the hydrogen bonding provides strong intermolecular attraction. The result is a strong, crystalline material. The particular structure drawn is called Nylon-66 because each amine and acid monomer contains six carbon atoms.

Nylons are used for rope, bristles, stockings, packaging, film, adhesives, gears, printing inks, and many other applications.

POLYMER RESEARCH

Having surveyed the various types of thermosetting and thermoplastic polymers, we should take a look at the research chemist who is involved in this field. How does he go about making wonderful new finds in this field? Actually, the polymer chemist now has a lot to go on. Discoveries have been made, extensive data have been recorded, and many theories have been proposed. Still the path to finding something really new is a long and arduous one. Usually the researcher is looking for a certain property in a plastic material. Someone, for instance, may need a clear plastic sheet which will resist certain chemicals and also possess particular qualities of strength and flexibility. The chemist may choose a class of compounds which roughly fits the specifications. Then he attempts to "tailor" the final product. We have already mentioned copolymerization. Inclusion of other monomers with the main monomer is one way in which properties can be varied. One type of copolymerization that might be employed is *graft polymerization*. Just as one piece of skin can be grafted onto another, so a section of polymer can be grafted onto another already-completed polymer. Here the ends of the molecule differ from the middle. Another type of copolymerization is called *block polymerization*. In this method, a chain is built up with alternating sections of different polymers. This also will lead to different properties. Another method is simply to mix varying amounts of different monomers and polymerize them simultaneously. An example is Nylon-12, which is made up of combined units of

$$\begin{array}{c} H \\ \diagdown \\ N-(CH_2)_{11}-C \diagup{O} \\ \diagup \\ H \end{array} \quad \begin{array}{c} O \\ \diagup \\ C \\ \diagdown \\ OH \end{array}$$

in which the head of one molecule attaches to the tail of another and yields a nylon that is hard and rigid. Mixing Nylon-12 and Nylon-6 monomers in a 50-50 proportion results in a polymer that is softer and much more flexible. This is due to the fact that the monomer units are arranged in a random fashion. As a result, the polar $-N-H$ and $>C=O$ groups do not "line up" and produce the strong intermolecular attraction. The chemist can also produce changes in structure and properties by means of various additives. These include plasticizers (materials used to produce more flow and workability), dye, and agents to produce resistance to ultraviolet light or to impart electrical conductivity, strength, chemical resistance, etc. Throughout his research program the chemist must make use of his testing and analytical laboratories. He must keep track of such properties as molecular weight, viscosity (resistance to flow), electrical conductivity, mechanical strength, carbon content, arrangement of atoms (which he can do, for example, through infrared analysis), and softening point. If he is successful in obtaining the special property he is seeking and still maintains the other properties at a satisfactory level, he will probably have a trial run performed and then turn the process over to the manufacturing department. I have omitted one factor of vital importance to the manufacturer—cost. If the sale price of the item cannot sufficiently exceed the cost of manufacture, the item will doubtlessly not be produced.

QUESTIONS AND PROJECTS

1. Compare addition and condensation polymerization. Give an example of each.

2. How does low-density polyethylene differ from high-density polyethylene?

3. Draw structures for polypropylene
a. With methyl groups arranged randomly
b. With methyl groups arranged alternately on either side of the chain
Compare the properties of each structure.

4. Compare the following methods of polymerization:
a. Bulk
b. Solution
c. Emulsion
d. Suspension

5. Draw structures for
a. Polymethyl acrylate
b. Polymethyl methalcylate

6. Make foam ball models of two short Teflon chains. Do these chains fit well together? What are the resultant properties?

7. List 10 common plastic products. Determine or predict the polymer used in each case.

8. Describe the steps taken by a polymer research chemist in developing a new polymer.

9. Draw the structure for
a. Nylon-55
b. Nylon-12
c. Dacron

10. What type of thermoplastic polymer structure exhibits
a. Crystallinity?
b. Amorphous condition?
c. Low softening point?
d. Hardness?

11. Discuss the effect of length of chain and interchain attraction on physical properties of thermoplastic resins.

12. What is polarity and how does it affect polymer properties?

13. Give uses for polyethylene and polypropylene. Compare the properties of these two polymers.

14. Look up the current production of acrylics. What is the largest application?

15. Polyvinylidene chloride, which is sold under the trade name Saran Wrap, has the following structure:

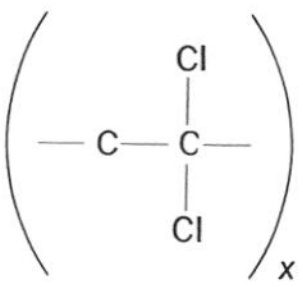

$$\left(-\ \underset{}{C}-\overset{\displaystyle Cl}{\underset{\displaystyle Cl}{C}}-\ \right)_x$$

Make foam ball models of short polyvinyl chloride chains and polyvinylidene chains.

12

FOOD ADDITIVES

In earlier chapters, we read that all living and inanimate things are composed of atoms and molecules in various simple and complex arrangements. The human body is, indeed, a very complex system of atoms and molecules arranged and reacting in a highly ordered manner. Since the body acts like a machine, it requires fuel to produce the energy needed for its own growth and activity. Food, which is the fuel, is also a collection of atoms bonded together in various arrangements. Some of these arrangements are assimilated by the body to be incorporated in its bones, muscles, organs, and blood. Such arrangements, which we can refer to as building blocks, are carbohydrates, fats, proteins, water, minerals, and vitamins. Therefore, to answer the question what chemistry has to do with food, we realize first that food itself is nothing but chemicals. However, the detailed structure and properties of various foods, although a very long and interesting story, is not the topic of this chapter. Instead we are going to consider the various chemicals that

◀ BY PERMISSION OF USDA.

are added, either intentionally or otherwise, to the food products that we consume. You have all heard of enriched flour and bread, of the addition of vitamin A to margarine, and of the addition of colors, flavors, and preservatives to many products. The kinds of chemicals added, the favorable results obtained, and the attendant problems created will be discussed.

Not too long ago, city populations were small and people lived for the most part in the country. They raised and ate their own vegetables, grain, and livestock. There were no shipment problems on the farm, and fresh food was always available. However, with the industrial revolution and the increase in urbanization, populations came to depend upon foods prepared, shipped, and stored by others. Foodstuffs had to be treated so that they would stay fresh, be free from dangerous micro-organisms, fulfill dietary requirements, please the eye and taste, and provide other special requirements as needed. This is how the use of chemicals comes into play. Chemical additives are used to prevent spoilage by contact with the air, to prevent or inhibit the growth of microbes, to change or enhance flavor and/or color, for aging purposes (flour is artificially aged), to make smooth uniform products, such as frozen desserts and instant hot chocolate, to hasten ripening (bananas and melons), to prevent sprouting (potatoes), and to produce other special characteristics, such as firmness or softness. Along with these intentional additives, there are other chemicals that find their way into your food. They include sanitizers and detergents used by the food processors in preparing our foods and the insecticides, fungicides, weed killers, plant and animal growth regulators, and related compounds used in agricultural production to protect plants and animals. The two classes, intentional additives and unintentional additives, will be discussed separately, and the topic of microorganisms and their inhibition will be saved until last.

INTENTIONAL ADDITIVES

COLORS AND FLAVORS

Why should color and flavor be important in a food product? A food chemist, in listing what is necessary for a well-balanced diet (proteins, carbohydrates, vitamins, etc.), might well omit all mention of color or flavor. Yet if a food product is not pleasing to the eye and the palate of the consumer, he may not eat it, and all its special nutritional values will be wasted.

The city dweller insists on food that closely resembles freshly butchered meat or freshly picked fruit and vegetables. Given the modern techniques of food processing, shipping, and storage, the preservation of original color and flavor would only be a coincidence. Therefore, the food industry must resort to coloring and flavoring agents. There are 2 or 3 hundred natural and synthetic flavoring agents approved by the FDA, but only a few coloring agents. It should be noted at this point that the FDA is the regulatory agency that supervises the use of chemicals in food and cosmetics as well as in drugs (recall Chap. 8 on drugs). Previous to 1958–1960, when the food additives and color additives amendments to the Federal Food and Drug Act were passed, the FDA could disapprove the use of a coloring or flavoring (or other) agent or else approve it without regard to the amount used in any product. To prevent the use of a possibly harmful chemical, the FDA had to provide all the data necessary to *prove* that the additive was unsafe. This practice was reversed by the amendments; the producer had to prove the safety of a compound before FDA approval could be granted. Moreover, the FDA was given authority to establish tolerances (upper limits of concentration of chemicals in food products) for safe use. Previous to the amendments there were some 19 colors on the approved list. One of these, called FD&C orange No. 1, ran into trouble in 1950 when a candy company produced a quantity of Halloween candy and tried to match the color of pumpkins. Severe gastrointestinal attacks were suffered by a number of children. This event helped to show that the law should include the regulation of quantity as well as identity of additive.

CARCINOGENIC AGENTS

Not long after, two other colors, FD&C yellow No. 3 and No. 4, were found to contain small amounts of beta-naphthylamine. (Remember that an amine has the functional group —NH$_2$. *Naphthyl* refers to a special double ring of carbon atoms, and *beta* indicates the position of the amine group on the ring system.) Moreover, it was shown that acid would react with these dyes to form more beta-naphthylamine. The reason for concern here was that beta-naphthylamine had been shown to produce cancer of the bladder; thus the dyes were dangerous for human consumption. As a consequence of this and similar situations, the food additive and color amendment forbade the addition of any known cancer-producing agent (carcinogen) or any agent which could be metabolized into a cancer-producing agent. Since the FDA had been given the authority to establish tolerances, carcinogens were assigned a zero tolerance. In all, almost half the previously approved coloring agents were banned as a result of additional toxicological and pharmacological data. The list of flavoring agents, which numbered in the hundreds, was also diminished as more detailed data were obtained. For instance, safrole, a constituent of the oil of sassafras, which was used to flavor root beer, was found to produce liver tumors in rats at fairly high levels. This ingredient was deleted from the approved list, and its use was discontinued.

I must point out that the questions what is a carcinogen, what amount of a carcinogen presents a hazard, and whether no amount or small amounts should be allowed in foods are quite a controversial subject. Manufacturers and scientists can present many creditable arguments that, indeed, all substances are toxic in certain amounts. Not long ago, you may recall that a hospital nurse preparing formulas for newborn babies mistakenly used salt instead of sugar. More than one death occurred. As far as carcinogenic evidence is concerned, data resulting from tests with animals may not be translatable to humans. Certain arsenic and chromium compounds are known to cause cancer in humans but do not appear to harm animals. Since this sort of difference does exist, it might well be that some compounds that are carcinogenic in animals may not be carcinogenic in humans. Furthermore, the analytical chemist working for the manufacturer may say in all honesty that a "zero tolerance" is not realistic. When we are considering, for instance, a pesticide that may remain in a food, the levels prescribed by the FDA are usually of the order of magnitude of a few parts of agent per million parts of food. With the advent of new techniques and improved instrumentation, the analyst can now measure parts per billion and even lower. Therefore, an instrument which is not too sensitive might indicate that there is zero concentration of an agent in a sample whereas another, more sensitive instrument might detect a very small trace amount. You can see that there is a real problem in defining zero tolerance.

Another argument is that there are suspected carcinogens in some natural foods. For instance, there are small amounts of safrole present in cinnamon and nutmeg. These and other natural foods, some people maintain, should undergo serious examination. The arguments of the manufacturers, who are doing a remarkable job of providing quality food products in ever larger quantities, are real and complex.

On the other hand, the consuming public has arguments of its own. Since there are many questions about the causes of cancer (and other degenerative diseases) and since there may be a cumulative effect in our bodies, which are exposed to many different possible carcinogens over long periods of time, many persons object to unnecessary exposure to any suspected carcinogenic agents. Indeed, this is the current status of the law in the United States. I might point out, however, that there is constant pressure by manufacturing groups to make the law more flexible in their favor.

ANTIOXIDANTS

Certain food products, especially fatty foods, spoil due to reaction with oxygen in the air. Lard, shortening, potato chips, crackers, and other foodstuffs require the addition of antioxidant compounds to prevent this spoilage. Butylated hydroxyanisole (BHA) and butylated hydroxytoluene (BHT) are commonly used antioxidants. [Both are derivatives of phenol (C_5H_6OH). Remember the phenol-formaldehyde polymers?] It was found that the inclusion of such a substance as citric acid enhances the effect of both these agents. The citric acid by itself was ineffective, but since it worked in combination with the antioxidant, it was called a *synergist* (something that works in cooperation with something else). However, it is now believed that the oxidation process is accelerated by the presence of metal in such forms as copper and iron salts and that the citric acid "ties up" the metal ions and prevents them from helping the spoiling processes. This "tying-up" action is often called *chelation*, a very important type of bonding that takes places in many chemical environments, including the human body. Remember that we can form ionic bonds by exchange of electrons and that we can form covalent bonds by sharing electrons through orbital overlapping.

Consider a molecule that could provide several bonds for one metal atom. This molecule would surround and trap the metal and prevent it from wandering about as a free ion. A compound that formed two bonds at one time could be pictured as a crab's claw grabbing the atom (hence

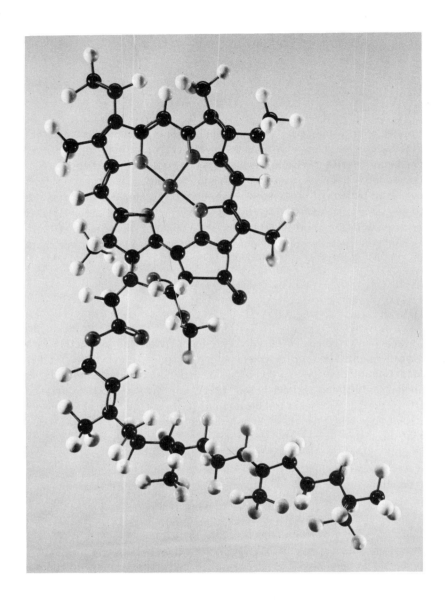

FIGURE 12–1   THE STRUCTURE OF CHLOROPHYLL. NOTICE HOW THE MAG-
NESIUM ATOM IS HELD BY CHELATION. (*BY PERMISSION OF
HARVARD UNIVERSITY NEWS OFFICE.*)

the term chelation, from the Greek word meaning crab). Some molecules can provide two bonds at a time, some three, four, five, six, or even more. Examples of chelate compounds that you know are hemoglobin (an iron atom enclosed in a large ring structure) and chlorophyll (very similar to the hemoglobin structure, but with magnesium in place of iron).

NUTRITIONAL SUPPLEMENTS

We all know that diseases such as pellagra, scurvy, night blindness, and rickets are caused by vitamin deficiencies. Further, problems such as endemic goiter, dental cavities, and anemia can be controlled by the use of proper minerals. (Minerals can be considered non-carbon-containing compounds, such as sodium fluoride, iron chloride, and magnesium sulfate. The carbon-containing compounds are called *organic* and the non-carbon-containing are called *inorganic*.) We also know that new foods and new processing methods often result in reduced vitamin and mineral content. Therefore, it becomes very important that certain vitamins and minerals be added or *returned* to our everyday foods.

Iodine in salt has been an extremely effective method of preventing goiter in the Americas, India, Southeast Asia, and Africa. Sodium fluoride (NaF), when added to water supplies deficient in natural fluorides, has been shown to reduce the prevalence of cavities by about 50 percent. Iron is added to wheat, flour, and other cereals to prevent nutritional anemia, which is a fairly common public health problem. Vitamins are added to certain foods, usually in an attempt to return the vitamin content to its normal level. For instance, in the milling of flour the grain kernel is broken and sifted. The white flour from the starch center, which has little mineral and no vitamin content, comes through first. This flour, however, has very good storage qualities as compared to flour which retains some of the outer coat. Next comes the flour with a yellowish tint and more protein. This is more starchy and is used in the preparation of macaroni and spaghetti. The germ of the kernel, which contains all the vitamins, oil, and starch necessary for sprouting the new plants, and the bran, the outside coating of the kernel, which is rich in minerals, are removed in the milling process. Replacing B-complex vitamins such as thiamine, riboflavin, and niacin as well as iron is called "enriching," and bread made from such flour is "enriched." The same problem and solution exists with polished rice. The addition of thiamine to polished rice is particularly important in countries such as China, Burma, India, and Vietnam where clinical beriberi still occurs. Other examples of the addition of vitamins to food are vitamin A to margarine and vitamin D to milk, fluid skim milk, and nonfat dry milk.

I have not mentioned the levels at which vitamins and minerals can be used. These are determined by the FDA, based upon the estimated food intake of the average person. Generally, nutrients possess a large margin of safety. However, indiscriminate use of vitamins and minerals is not at all indicated. We are aware that large doses of sodium fluoride can be harmful and even fatal. With respect to vitamins, too, caution is advisable. Recently a respected pediatrician pointed out that too much vitamin D in fortified food may be linked to birth defects. The excess vitamin D has the effect of making calcium more available in the blood stream and thus more easily absorbed.

OTHER INTENTIONAL ADDITIVES

It would take several chapters to list and discuss the many chemicals that are used in processing, ripening, prevention of ripening, bleaching, and sanitizing, as well as in controlling moisture, dryness, acidity, foaming, settling, hardening, etc. The food producers are using these agents to provide us with nutritious, appealing foods in the quantities that we require. For instance, to maintain sanitary conditions in the processing equipment, germ-killing detergents must be used. Of course, the manufacturer must be careful that this detergent is thoroughly rinsed from the equipment and does not find its way into the food products.

UNINTENTIONAL ADDITIVES

The role of insecticides, herbicides, fungicides, plant growth regulators, and other pesticides in agricultural chemistry has been discussed. The significance for this chapter is that small amounts of most pesticides remain in the plant or animal products. Some pesticides, especially insecticides, are very poisonous substances and must be handled accordingly. To obtain approval of a pesticide, the manufacturer must show the Department of Agriculture that the product will be effective and safe for those using it and for other people and animals nearby and that it will not harm other crops. If, under the conditions of its use, no residue remains in the crop, the FDA is not involved. However, if a residue remains, FDA approval must be obtained, and a tolerance level in the food product may be set. If the compound is shown to be carcinogenic or if the compound might be metabolized in the body to a carcinogen, a zero tolerance is imposed. A special case is milk: a zero tolerance has been established for *any* pesticide. This situation has created a difficult competition between two branches of the government—the Department of Agriculture and the FDA. Not long ago two pesticides, dieldrin and heptachlor, were given a zero tolerance by the FDA. They were being used on alfalfa, and the alfalfa was being fed to dairy cows. It had been shown that such cows could transmit residues to the milk. The Department of Agriculture, on the other hand, insisted that under proper use no residue would remain on the alfalfa. However, the residues were found, many milk-selling permits were suspended, and the Department of Agriculture finally withdrew registration of the two pesticides for use in alfalfa. You will recall that a similar problem existed with the weed killer aminotriazole and the cranberries. Aminotriazole had been found to produce thyroid cancer in test animals and was being found on cranberries treated at the wrong time of year.

DDT

A great deal is said about DDT (dichlorodiphenyl-trichloroethane) and other chlorinated pesticides. Such agents are oil-soluble and thus can be stored in body fat, that is, in the liver, kidneys, and intestines. Since food products contain small amounts of DDT, all of us are gradually building up a supply of it in our bodies. Another factor which makes this chemical more of a threat is that it is very stable toward atmospheric conditions. Most pesticides will react with moisture and oxygen and be converted into other products and carried away. DDT, however, is very persistent and will usually remain in an area long after it has been used. It can thus find its way into water supplies. Persons working near large concentrations of DDT have been observed to tolerate dosages approximately 200 times greater than normal. Although this is somewhat reassuring, long-term effects from one generation to another have yet to be checked. Avoidance of unnecessary or excessive use of DDT and other pesticides is certainly indicated.

ACCIDENTAL POISONING

Before leaving the topic of pesticides and their residual hazard in food, I should mention the ever-present possibility of accidental poisoning. Food can sometimes be sprayed with pesticides contrary to printed directions. Occasionally, products are sprayed in error just prior to harvesting, with the result that a dangerous amount of pesticide is present. Pesticides are commonly available in the home for the family garden. Here, special precautions must be taken. Some phosphorous-containing organic insecticides, such as parathion, are very deadly. Recently, accidents have occurred in which parathion containers were mixed in with flour shipments. The flour became contaminated and many persons eating the bread died. The problem here is one of proper warning and labeling, and careful shipping regulations.

MICROORGANISMS AND INHIBITORS

This chapter would not be complete without a consideration of the biological hazards of food. Such hazards are not unrelated to chemicals because they can often be controlled or inhibited by chemical additives.

STAPH

The most common type of food poisoning is caused by a toxin produced by staphylococci, bacteria which are carried by a large portion of the human population. Staph has the ability to grow in salt solutions whereas other bacteria are likely to be killed. Thus, curing meat or cheese with salt may actually encourage the growth of the bacteria. They do not grow at refrigeration temperatures, but do multiply rapidly at room temperature. Symptoms involve nausea, vomiting, abdominal pains, and diarrhea. A particular problem with staphylococci is that the bacteria may be destroyed by some method, but the toxin produced can remain behind to do its damage.

SALMONELLA

Another serious biological food problem is known as salmonella food poisoning. There are some 800 strains of the salmonella bacillus, most of which live and grow in the intestines of man and animal. There is no toxin involved here; the organism does the damage directly. Salmonellosis, although usually not fatal, is very uncomfortable. Headache, abdominal pain, chills, faintness, fever, and vomiting are some of the symptoms that may persist for up to a week. Salmonella outbreaks are usually traced to animals or animal products. However, the disease can be easily spread by careless carriers, especially food handlers.

BOTULISM

The most deadly form of food poison is the toxin produced by the heat-resistant clostridium botulinum. A botulism victim has little chance of survival if he does not obtain an antitoxin within two days. Symptoms are similar to those of polio. The nervous system is attacked, and abdominal pain, nausea, double vision, and difficulty in speech and breathing are experienced. The botulism microorganisms are very resistant to heat and flourish in the absence of air (they are anaerobic). Botulism was more common in the "good old days" when home canning was more in fad. Modern food processing has cut down on the instances of botulism poisoning but it still occurs.

INHIBITORS

What can be done to prevent such biological food poisoning? Certainly, routine sanitary precautions should be observed in all phases of food processing. Pasteurization by heating or by irradiating with ultraviolet or other penerating radiation, removal of water, refrigeration, and other physical methods should be used wherever possible. Chemicals can also be used to good advantage.

An apparently harmless compound, benzoic acid, is used to control bacterial or mold growth in margarine, acid fruits and vegetables, and confections. Sulfur dioxide gas, SO_2, is probably the most versatile food preservative. It is used as a gas or in the form of sulfurous acid or sulfites. Note that sulfur dioxide when dissolved in water forms sulfurous acid shown on p. 142 in the first equation. Alkalies (also called *bases*), such as calcium hydroxide, can react with this acid to form the salt calcium sulfite (see the second equation below). This type of reaction, in which an acid and a base form water and a salt, is called *neutralization*. When you take an antacid formulation to relieve excess stomach acidity, this is the type of reaction taking place:

$$SO_2 + H_2O \longrightarrow H_2SO_3 \qquad Ca(OH)_2 + H_2SO_3 \longrightarrow 2(H_2O) + CaSO_3$$

Sulfur dioxide	Water	Sulfurous acid		Calcium hydroxide	Sulfurous acid		Water	Calcium sulfite

Sulfites are easily oxidized and excreted from the body and present a hazard only in large amounts. Since large concentrations usually affect the color and flavor of foods, sulfite poisoning will probably not be a frequent occurrence. This agent is used routinely in many countries for preparing preserves and jams, wine, and dried fruits.

Sorbic acid, propionic acid, and sodium diacetate are used extensively as mold and yeast inhibitors in bread and cheese. Nitrates, which are considered indispensable in meat curing, appear to retard the growth of anaerobes. Nitrites have been used for some time as a food preservative. Experimentation with antibiotics as a means of food preservation is receiving a great deal of attention. However, problems such as the development of resistant strains of organisms and sensitization of humans receiving repeated low-level quantities has prompted a conservative attitude toward this application.

In summary, there are many types of chemical agents added to foods, both intentionally and unintentionally. To expand the food production of the world in an attempt to keep up with the population explosion, the use of chemicals in growing, preparing, and storing foodstuffs is unavoidable. The manufacturers and processors must concurrently match this pace with efforts to protect the consumers.

QUESTIONS AND PROJECTS

1. Make a list of the types of foods, vitamins, and minerals necessary in our diet.

2. List five disorders due to lack of a certain vitamin or mineral.

3. From your kitchen or grocery store compile a list of 10 packaged food products which do *not* contain an artificial color or flavor or a preservative.

4. What is meant by zero tolerance? In what cases does it apply? What difficulty is there in determining it?

5. What would you recommend concerning the consumption of natural foods that contain suspected carcinogens?

6. Why is it difficult to determine what is a carcinogen for man?

7. Describe
a. Synergist
b. Chelation
c. Antioxidant
d. Aerobic microorganism

8. Where sodium fluoride is used in municipal water supplies, what is its concentration? What is considered a hazarodus level of consumption?

9. Describe the production of any food product. What chemicals are used in the process? Which are intentional additives? Why are they used?

10. Compare the following types of food poisoning and discuss means of prevention:
a. Staph
b. Salmonella
c. Botulism

11. Give a sample structure for each of the following:
a. Carbohydrate
b. Fat
c. Protein
d. Mineral
e. Vitamin

12. If your foods were different in color but tasted the same and were identical in every other respect, would you still eat them? Discuss.

13. Tell about a recent incident of food poisoning and, if possible, state the cause.

14. Compile a list of natural foods which contain suspected carcinogens.

15. List five common foods to which are added nutritional supplements. Name the latter.

13

WATER POLLUTION

Now that we have considered the topic of pure food and its various intentional and unintentional additives, it would certainly be appropriate and profitable for us to give some attention to the topic of water. In taking for granted the availability of pure water, we all tend to overlook its importance to us as a life-giving and life-preserving molecule. Certainly, when we stop to reflect, we realize that water is indeed essential to us, not only for the life processes, but for other secondary purposes which make our living easier and more enjoyable. As we study in this chapter the supply of water and its various uses, we will realize that the most practical solution to the problem of providing water for future generations lies in the *reuse* of water. Furthermore, this reuse can only be effected if pollution is kept under control.

WATER STRUCTURE

Before we start our discussion of water supply, pollutants, and the treatment of polluted water, we should first look at the water molecule itself

and learn something about its structure and properties. Water is composed of two hydrogen atoms attached to an oxygen atom (H $\diagup$ O $\diagdown$ H).
The bond between each hydrogen atom and the oxygen atom is a covalent or shared bond made up of an electron from a hydrogen atom and
an electron from the oxygen atom. Hydrogen and oxygen each have an
attraction for electrons. However, oxygen's attraction (its electronegativity) is greater than that of hydrogen, and hence oxygen gets a better
share of the pair of electrons in each bond. This gives the oxygen owner-
ship of more electric charges than before bonding, when it had the
same number of electrons and protons, whose charges cancel. Now,
since the water molecule is "bent" and since the oxygen is hogging the
shared electrons, the oxygen atom has a more negative charge than the
hydrogen atoms. The molecule is then said to be "polar," with one
portion negatively charged and the other positively charged. Suppose
two molecules of water approach one another; as you might guess, the
negative portion of one molecule will attract the positive portion of the
other, in intermolecular attraction like that encountered in our study of
the polymers. Further, you will recall that we said there was a still
greater attraction between water molecules than we could account for
by electrical attraction alone; we called this condition hydrogen bonding.

WATER PROPERTIES

The strong intermolecular attraction brought about by this special bonding largely determines water's physical properties. Or to put it another
way, if water did not experience hydrogen bonding, its freezing point
would probably be 148°F below zero, and its boiling point would probably be 112°F below zero. This would be a completely different water
problem!

The heat content of water is another physical property that is of great
importance to life on earth. Moisture in the air absorbs radiation from
the sun and releases it as energy at night, thus moderating the extremes
of temperature from day to night. The reason that water can do such a
good job of absorbing and releasing energy is also related to hydrogen
bonding. When ice is melted, the rigidly arranged molecules are loosened
and removed from their crystalline lattice and allowed freedom so that
they can slip and slide over one another in the liquid state. Similarly,

when liquid water is vaporized, energy is provided to separate the molecules one from another and force them into a relatively isolated condition known as the gaseous state. During both transitions, the solid-to-liquid and the liquid-to-gas, energy must be provided to overcome the intermolecular attractions, particularly the hydrogen bonding. Since the vaporizing of liquid is more of a drastic change involving the complete separation of all molecules, there is considerably more energy required than for the melting of ice. Water, then, serves a very valuable purpose in moderating temperature changes. Those of us who live near a large body of water are familiar with this since we experience cooler summers and warmer winters. The water which has absorbed summer's heat is slow to release it and gives up a portion of it during the winter. Similarly, the water cooled during the winter is slow to warm up, and summer breezes are cooled as they pass over its surface. Without the moderating effect of water against changes in energy on the earth's surface, life, as we know it, could not exist.

EARTH'S WATER SUPPLY—THE HYDROLOGICAL CYCLE

Let us now consider where the earth's water is, where it goes, and how much of it is available as fresh water. There is actually a very large supply of water on the earth. However, most of the water is salt water while the fresh water very often is in the wrong places at the wrong times. Since the oceans cover more than 70 percent of the earth's surface, it is not surprising that approximately 98 percent of the water on the earth is sea water. Less than 2 percent is in the form of ice, a fraction of one percent is fresh water, and an even smaller fraction of one percent is in the form of water vapor in the atmosphere. Although these figures remain fairly constant, the water itself does not stay put. It is continually evaporating from water surfaces, forming clouds, and returning to earth in the form of rain, sleet, or snow, as it becomes part of ice caps or glaciers or runs off into streams, lakes, or underground reservoirs. Water from these waterways eventually finds its way to the sea and the process is repeated. This is called the *water cycle* or the *hydrological cycle*.

There are some interesting facts about this cycle. For instance, consider the evaporation of water from the largest sources, the oceans. It is estimated that about 50 percent of the sun's energy at sea level is

FIGURE 13–1   GLACIAL ICE MEETING THE SEA. (*BY PERMISSION OF ESSA.*)

used up in evaporating sea water. (Of course, we know that the salts in sea water remain behind and only pure water is evaporated). As pointed out previously, the energy removed from the sun's radiation is stored in the water vapor as the *latent heat of vaporization,* the heat needed to vaporize the water. This is a very important contribution to the heat bank of the atmosphere. Remember that we said that water is a very important factor in moderating the temperature of the earth. It is also estimated that about 75 percent of the evaporated sea water is eventually deposited on polar ice caps and glaciers, with only approximately 25 percent falling on other land areas. As for the water that does fall on land, you may be surprised to learn that a very high percentage is reevaporated back into the atmosphere. Some is evaporated immediately, some gradually from streams and ponds; and some is absorbed by the roots of trees and other vegetation and then is transpiration-evaporated from the foliage. The water that remains available for our use collects in ponds, streams, and reservoirs and percolates down into porous underground beds which act as reservoirs (called aquifers). The large amounts of water stored here are not subject to the severe evaporation losses suffered by ordinary reservoirs. Moreover, undergound water often travels great distances, saving the very high cost of water transportation. A thorough understanding of this hydrological cycle and the many interrelated variables involved may someday allow us to control or at least influence some portions of the cycle. Progress in this area could produce some valuable solutions to the water supply problem.

WATER SHORTAGE

And we do have a water supply problem! I am sure there are few people who have not suffered or read about one of the serious water shortages in the United States in recent years. The population explosion can, of course, be quoted as a reason. However, when we consider that the population of the United States has approximately doubled since 1900 while the water consumption has increased from 8 to 10 times, we realize that population alone does not explain the problem. More important is our new way of life. We demand and enjoy the fruits of our ever-improving technology. Making farms out of deserts requires tremendous quantities of water, as does the manufacture of textiles, steel, chemicals, and food; in addition, we as individuals are using far more water than our grandparents or great-grandparents. We have automatic washers, swimming pools, car washes, garbage disposals, and extensive and thirsty lawns. In the United States in 1900, the rate of water consumption was about 40 billion gallons per day. By the year 2000, it could run as high as 900 billion gallons per day. Taking into consideration that during a year of average rainfall the United States receives a resultant streamflow of about 1,250 billion gallons per day and keeping in mind that less than half this streamflow can be made available for use, we see that there is a frightening possibility that we could run out of water. What can we do? First, we must examine the 900-billion-gallon figure given above. In breaking down this amount, we find that the largest amounts will be used by industry, steam, and power supply. Next in line is the amount used for irrigation, and last, but certainly most important, is municipal use.

It is important to distinguish types of water consumption in which the used water is lost by evaporation to the atmosphere from those in which it is recovered for further use. Irrigation water suffers severe evaporation and transportation losses (approximately 70 percent). On the other hand, steam and electric power lose less than one percent of the water employed. Similarly, municipal and manufacturing uses waste from about 8 to 15 percent. Thus, if we consider water-usage figures on the basis of actual water consumed, they are not quite so alarming. Implicit, however, in this pacifying statement is the assumption that the water returned for use is *reusable*. Hence our deep concern about pollution. Only if we use our water wisely, while preserving its cleanliness, can we hope to brighten the gloomy water picture of the future.

HOW TO INCREASE THE FRESH WATER SUPPLY

NEW SOURCES

Before we examine various pollution problems, we should briefly review what other steps are to be taken to prevent a future water shortage. I am referring to ways of increasing the fresh water supply. Scientists have been trying for many years to control or at least influence the weather. If we could produce rain where and when we wanted it, our problems would be at an end. Indeed, some success at "seeding" clouds with dry ice (solid carbon dioxide) or crystals of silver iodide has been recorded. These particles apparently provide nuclei on which moisture droplets can condense, grow in size, and eventually fall to the earth.

Progress has been slow, and even if success were near at hand, one wonders if the political problems could be overcome. Some areas are sure to resent floods brought on by "rain controllers." Resorts and similar businesses would also be unsympathetic to frequent rainy periods. However, research in this area continues, and there is hope that it will produce useful results. The building of large and small dams on rivers and tributaries continues. Some states, California for example, are building complex reservoir and aqueduct systems for transporting water from wet to dry areas, and similar projects involving more than one state have been accomplished or are being planned. Such arrangements are usually very difficult to make since the states with the most water are very reluctant to share their liquid treasure. A huge project has been proposed for the collection and transportation of water from Canada down to the Great Lakes and beyond, through the Rocky Mountains, and down into Mexico. Unfortunately, the jealousies and political differences among countries are even greater than among states, and such a project will probably require a long time for fruition, if it can be done at all. Removing salt from sea water or removing sea water from salt is now being done on an economically feasible basis. Water at prices comparable to existing prices is now available from these *desalination plants*. The chief method used imitates nature. Recall that the sun evaporates the water from the sea, leaving the salts behind. Energy from atomic power plants extracts pure water from sea water by the same process, which we call *distillation*. Another method used is called *electrodialysis*. In this method, the positive sodium ions and negative chloride ions diffuse through a plastic membrane toward negatively and positively charged electrodes. This leaves behind pure water which is then drawn off. Generally, much larger amounts can be produced by the distillation method. However, in areas of the world where there is practically no usable water, even a little is a lot.

CONSERVE FRESH WATER

Many avenues are being followed to conserve our fresh water. Research is being conducted to find inexpensive ways of lining irrigation ditches and reservoirs to prevent seepage and of spraying reservoirs with special chemicals to form nontoxic continuous films that inhibit evaporation. Even the possibility of removing or replacing plants that transpire excessively is being studied.

CONTROL POLLUTION AND REUSE WATER

It is evident, then, that we have three ways of offsetting the impending water crisis. We can provide new supplies, conserve what we have, and control pollution so that we may reuse our water. Building dams and transporting water must be continued. This, however, can only be done within our means, and it is very expensive. Desalination plants are a wonderful result of technology and a demonstration of the peaceful use of nuclear energy. Cities located on the sea should not lack pure water, again assuming that we can afford the great expense of installing desalination facilities. Conservation will certainly continue to be an important aspect of the problem. Prevention of seepage and evaporation can save a great deal of fresh water. Moreover, it has been repeatedly suggested that all users of water be metered and charged a much higher rate than previously. Perhaps if we paid a realistic price for this precious commodity, we would not be as wasteful as we are. Finally, the most practical and most economical way to ensure that our use of water does not exceed our supply in years to come is to reuse our water. This requires that the water must not become so polluted by either domestic or industrial waste that it cannot be economically purified. Thus, it is imperative that we learn what types of pollution we face and how they can be controlled.

NATURE'S PURIFICATION PROCESS

Scientists are usually wise enough to learn from a source of greater knowledge. Certainly the greatest fountain of knowledge is nature, and we continue to learn much just by careful observation. To begin a study of pollution and pollution removal, we may simply observe how a stream that receives domestic sewage purifies itself. I have specified domestic sewage purposely since industrial wastes usually present special problems. The organic materials contained in domestic sewage are capable of biochemical decomposition to stable inorganic structures such as nitrite, nitrate, sulfate, phosphate, and bicarbonate. This decomposition is carried out by the various bacteria and other organisms present in natural water. Where the waste is not too concentrated, the organisms that operate with the aid of dissolved oxygen perform *aerobic degradation*. In areas of excessive waste, organisms which can attack the organic matter without the aid of dissolved oxygen conduct *anaerobic degradation,* a process which results in foul odors due to the formation of gases such as hydrogen sulfide, a very toxic gas which has the odor of rotten eggs.

Since oxygen is involved in the aerobic degradation of organic pollutants, the amount of waste is measured by what is called *biochemical oxygen demand* (BOD). The more waste there is, the greater the amount of oxygen necessary for degradation through the action of the aerobic organisms. Hence, the BOD reflects the rate at which dissolved oxygen will be consumed. There are two stages in a stream's self-purification. In the first, close to the point of entrance of the raw sewage, there is a high BOD due to the large concentration of degradable compounds. This, of course, draws upon the reserve of dissolved oxygen. (If the BOD is great enough, the dissolved oxygen can be completely consumed and hence only anaerobic degradation can take place.) As we proceed farther downstream, the dissolved oxygen continues to drop until reaeration begins to offset the consumption. Thereafter the oxygen level tends to improve. Farther downstream there is a second stage wherein the nitrogen is converted by bacteria to nitrites and nitrates. This stage does not require as much dissolved oxygen.

SANITARY TREATMENT

Sanitary treatment plant processes are based upon the same principles of biochemical waste degradation that are observed taking place in natural waters. There are methods involving primary and secondary stages as well as combinations of primary and secondary stages. Both aerobic and anaerobic decompositions are utilized. Primary treatment involves some sort of holding tank where the sewage is allowed to settle for a while. Here there is a very large BOD; the dissolved oxygen is used up and anaerobic decomposition takes place. The organic matter is only partly broken down in this step. In the secondary treatment the primary effluent is passed through sand or stone filters where there is good contact with the air. Aerobic oxidation takes place, and the organic matter is converted to stable inorganic salts. A very common method of treatment which combines the two steps is known as the *activated sludge method.* Here the filtered sewage is placed in tanks into which air is blown. Porous clumps of sewage, called *floc*, develop. This floc, which has a high filtering and absorption power, carries the bacteria and brings it quickly into intimate contact with the oxidizable materials. A sludge develops, which can be further digested, and an effluent also develops, which is usually given a final treatment with chlorine to destroy any harmful bacteria remaining.

LIFE CYCLES IN NATURAL WATERS

Treatment plants and natural water purification, then, appear to be fairly uncomplicated. Why then this fuss about water pollution? So far, we have limited our discussion to domestic sewage in not too great a concentration and have omitted complicating factors including industrial pollution. Let us look again at the natural stream and consider a few of the numerous factors involved. The two stages, as outlined, seem relatively simple, but actually the entire process of natural water self-purification is a very delicate balance of many factors. There are many types of aquatic life, such as bacteria, algae, protozoa, mollusks, insects, and fish. Each of these has its own special job to perform and will do so within certain limits. For instance, the bacteria can attack various types of organic matter and can assimilate certain structures. Algae can utilize some of the products of decomposition and, in addition, through photosynthesis, can provide oxygen and carbohydrates for utilization by other aquatic life.

Each creature and component of the water performs its own function, and all functions seem to be interrelated. If one of the team members is removed by some chemical or physical condition, the entire process of stream purification can be upset and a serious pollution problem can develop. For instance, an increase in stream temperature, which might be caused by industrial discharge of spent cooling waters, will increase the rate of biochemical reactions, thus increasing the BOD, while at the same time decreasing the amount of dissolved oxygen. (Gases are generally less soluble in hot water than in cold. For example, as it warms up a bottle of soda soon loses its "fizz" of dissolved carbon dioxide gas.) In water that is receiving a great deal of waste, this action might result in septic conditions. Likewise, if a chemical with high bactericidal properties is injected into a stream, the useful bacteria can be killed off, with the result that decomposition may become negligible.

Algae can be both helpful and harmful. These tiny plants can provide oxygen and food and can consume some of the soluble products of degradation, particularly nitrogen and phosphorus compounds. If too much silt or suspended matter is discharged into a stream, sunlight, needed for plant growth, is blocked out and quantities of algae will die. They then become part of the organic waste matter and help to increase the BOD. The same situation exists when too much algae growth occurs. An increase in plant nutrients, particularly the phosphorus from detergents and other industrial formulations, results in large crops of algae which choke each other out, thus providing more demand for oxygen at that point. In addition to increasing the BOD, excessive algae can result in various tastes in our drinking water. This is why reservoirs are treated with copper sulfate—to control algae growth.

The foregoing are but a few examples of the upsets that can occur in the self-purification process of natural waters. The study of chemical, biological, and physical conditions of natural waters is called *limnology*, and the expert is called a *limnologist*. As technology continues to produce new insecticides, detergents, herbicides, and other industrial chemicals, the study of the effects on polluted waters becomes more complex and more necessary. Limnologists will continue to be in great demand both by manufacturers who make voluntary attempts to prevent water problems and by enforcement agencies who must detect and enforce measures to prevent them.

TYPES OF WASTE

All waste can be classified into two groups: degradable and nondegradable. Degradable wastes are organic structures such as those found in domestic sewage which, as we have seen, readily undergo biochemical decomposition. Nondegradable wastes include inorganic salts, radioactive wastes, and organic structures which are very resistant to degradation. Water that is used for irrigation is in running contact with the soil for a long period of time and picks up a considerable amount of salts, particularly sodium chloride, which cannot be removed by biochemical treatment and are thus classified as nondegradable. Radio-active salts, particularly from atomic explosions, can find their way into drinking water and present a real hazard. However, since the cessation of atmospheric tests, this source of pollution is of little concern. (More will be said of radioactivity in Chap. 16.) Certain industrial chemicals, such as the insecticide DDT, are very resistant to degradation.

The industrial pollutants contribute the major portion of the nonde-gradable class and deserve special consideration. As mentioned before, industry has performed wonders for our modern civilization, but it has also created some problems. There are four large producers of industrial pollution: the steel, textile, paper, and food processing industries.

PAPER INDUSTRY

The pulp and paper industries, which produce paper and paperboard products, have been growing and continue to grow at a very healthy rate. Unfortunately, despite the efforts of these manufacturers to con-trol the wastes from their processes, the volume of pollution continues to grow. The waste, which is the runoff from the step which separates the lignin from the cellulose, is either an acidic sulfite liquor or an alkaline effluent, depending upon the particular process used. The sulfite liquor is a mixture of sulfurous acid (H_2SO_3) and salts of sulfurous acid. An alkaline effluent could be an alkali such as calcium hydroxide [$Ca(OH)_2$]. With waste liquor, whether an acidic sulfate or an alkaline liquor, there is an excessive oxygen demand (BOD) placed upon the water into which it is ejected. If the demand is too great, as it often is near manufacturing sites, septic conditions can result, and fish and plant life can disappear.

TEXTILE, STEEL, FOOD, AND OTHER INDUSTRIES

Similarly, the textile industry produces its own share of pollution. The pretreatment and bleaching of cotton, flax, hemp, and wool produce waste mixtures containing oils, dirt, bacteria, and emulsifying agents. The steel companies donate to our waterways millions of gallons of

FIGURE 13–2   *ANYBODY FOR A SWIM? (BY PERMISSION OF FEDERAL WATER POLLUTION CONTROL ADMINISTRATION.)*

acids, lime, grease, iron salts, and oil. The food-processing industries unload entrails and washings containing bacteria and various agricultural chemicals. Refineries and chemical plants are dumping dyes, oil, waste solvents, grease, cyanides, and other unpleasant and noxious chemicals.

All these wastes are creating a BOD in the waters into which they are being discharged. In addition, many are creating an unsightly as well as an unhealthy environment. Anything which can upset the numerous and complicated chemical and biological processes involved in self-purification is producing water that is unfit for reuse by industry; unfit for swimming, boating, fishing; and most important of all, unfit for human consumption. With the demands for usable water increasing as fast as they are, we must combat this needless waste of one of our most precious natural resources. What can be done?

TECHNICAL SOLUTIONS

Technically, we do not have all the answers. As pointed out above, the purification processes of nature, or of man as copied from nature, are quite complex. Involved are many chemical structures both in living and nonliving systems. Since the interrelations are so complex, we do not understand the effect of all the many variables involved. When a new chemical is synthesized, its physical and chemical properties are just beginning to be investigated. If this new chemical is injected into a purification system, it may completely upset the delicate balance. The limnologist may discover that some link in the biochemical chain has been broken but may not be able to establish the reason. On the other hand, a new chemical may not create any problem at all. The days are past when the use of natural waters for the dumping of raw domestic or industrial waste was permitted. All wastes must undergo treatment. Domestic sewage treatment methods are established, and though they are undergoing continued improvement, they are adequate and efficient. However, if industrial wastes are indiscriminately injected into a domestic waste treatment plant, complete breakdown of the degradation process is likely to take place. Generally, some sort of special treatment facilities have to be constructed, perhaps in conjunction with a municipal sewage treatment plant. Often the best solution is for the manufacturing plant to build and operate its own treatment facility. This can sometimes result in recovery of waste chemicals and reuse of large volumes of water which were previously rejected.

Many industrialists and scientists are also studying ways to eliminate or alleviate the problems. One instance is the detergent problem mentioned earlier. Synthetic detergents, as they were formerly synthesized, efficiently resisted bacterial attack in septic tanks and municipal treatment plants. The result was that the undecomposed detergents in the effluents from the waste disposal processes were finding their way into ground and surface water supplies. People in some areas actually witnessed foam coming out of their faucets. A representative degradation-resistant structure is the following:

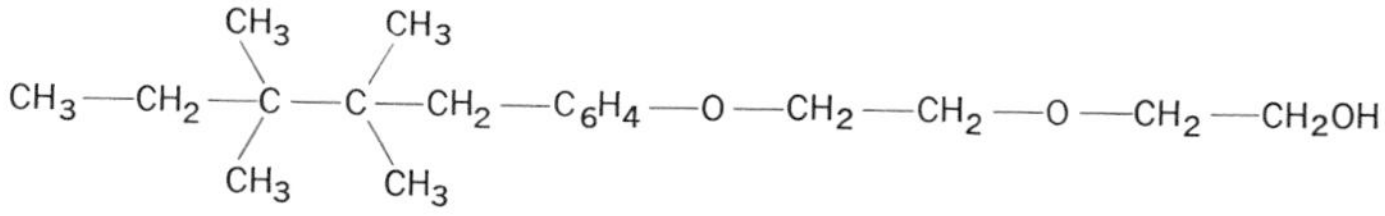

$$CH_3 - CH_2 - \underset{\underset{CH_3}{|}}{\overset{\overset{CH_3}{|}}{C}} - \underset{\underset{CH_3}{|}}{\overset{\overset{CH_3}{|}}{C}} - CH_2 - C_6H_4 - O - CH_2 - CH_2 - O - CH_2 - CH_2OH$$

This arrangement of atoms has detergent properties or, as we say, is a surface-active agent. This is so because one end of the molecule, the end with the oxygen, is similar to water, H—OH, and thus tends to dissolve in water. The other end is strictly hydrocarbon (hydrogen and carbon atoms) and thus tends to dissolve in such things as oil and grease. Thus, one end of the molecule is attracted to grease or dirt and the other end to water; the dirt is then transferred from the shirt or trousers to the water and is eventually rinsed away. (More discussion of this effect will be given in Chap. 15.)

The bringing together of the water molecules with the non-water material takes place at the surface of the water molecules. This explains the term "surface activity." There are many structures which exhibit this property to varying degrees. Their common characteristic is that there is a water-soluble portion and a non-water-soluble portion in the molecule.

The reason this kind of structure was not being degraded is that the bacteria found it "undigestible." Apparently bacteria can chew up atoms that are attached in a straight chain but either cannot or will not break down a branched chain.

$$CH_3 - CH_2 - CH_2 - \qquad \text{Straight chain}$$

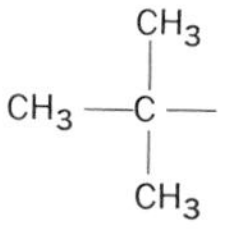

$$CH_3 - \underset{\underset{CH_3}{|}}{\overset{\overset{CH_3}{|}}{C}} - \qquad \text{Branched chain}$$

The problem has been solved by converting all branched chains into straight chains. For instance, the structure above now becomes the following:

$$CH_3 - (CH_2)_8 - C_6H_4 - OCH_2 - CH_2 - OCH_2 - CH_2 - OH$$

This structure is readily biodegradable. The voluntary conversion of all detergent structures to biodegradable structures is one example of the cooperation of science and industry without the necessity of federal control.

A unique solution to the problem of the disposal of acid wastes from iron pickling operations is being tested. It involves the evaporation of the spent acid with the concurrent recovery of reusable acid and the pro-

FIGURE 13-3   ALGAE ARE BEING USED TO RECLAIM WASTE WATER IN THIS EXPERIMENTAL POND. (BY PERMISSION OF NASA.)

duction of iron salts. It is possible that the value of the recovered salts and acid may balance the cost of the treatment.

Another area of research which holds promise for the elimination or control of certain types of pollutants is the study of algae. These microscopic plants, which are a part of the biochemical chain in natural water purification, can be a help or a nuisance, as we have seen. Preliminary results indicate that certain algae can assimilate various metal ions under the proper conditions. Making use of these algae economically feasible could be a great contribution to the fight against water pollution.

POLITICAL SOLUTIONS

So much for technical solutions which are being continually investigated. What about political solutions? We have seen that polluting natural waters with either domestic sewage or industrial waste is dangerous and that cleaning up polluted water is difficult and in many cases impossible. Therefore, the only real solution is to *prevent* pollution. Domestic sewage must be treated either in private septic tanks (if the area is not too populated, if the land provides the proper drainage, and if no water supply is endangered by the runoff) or in municipal treatment plants. Likewise, industrial waste must be treated in separate municipal plants or in their own facilities. The federal government, under the Water Quality Act of 1965, has made available numerous grants to communities to help with the construction of their domestic treatment plants. In addition, the government provides grants to industries to subsidize research programs on developing methods for treating their wastes. Municipal treatment has come a long way in a short time. However, correction of industrial pollution is lagging. I pointed out that many industries are striving to correct their own pollution problems. On the other hand, there are many others who use their influence to maintain the status quo. The Water Quality Act has set federal standards on interstate water purity. Cleaning up rivers that run from state to state has been extremely difficult in the past because each state had its own set of standards. Enforcement of these federal standards will, of course, be the test of their value. Some industrial firms have enormous political and economic power especially in communities which depend primarily upon these industries for employment. The favorite response from such a firm to a plea for correction of industrial pollution is "Too expensive. We will have to move to another location." How then is cooperation to be gained? The federal government is trying to comply with the popular request to correct a degenerating situation. State and local governments try also, but some do not try hard enough. Those that do face unbelievable enforcement problems. For a thorough job of interstate policing, the federal government will require a huge staff and a correspondingly large budget. In the end, the answer can only come from enlightened and spirited citizens.

ONE TOWN'S VICTORY OVER INDUSTRIAL POLLUTION

I would like to close this chapter with a small example of what a militant public can do. A small town in New England has a beautiful river which empties into the Long Island Sound. Marring its beauty and attacking its wildlife were the effluent wastes from a wire mill and a foundry. Persistent requests for termination of this industrial pollution were turned down because the town had no municipal treatment plant for its own domestic sewage, and it was well known that much raw domestic sewage was also defiling the river. Finally, with the assistance of a federal grant, a town treatment plant was installed. Then requests were made that the two industries join in and stop their pollution. These were turned down on the grounds that it was too expensive and that relocation would probably result. The town government refused to get involved. Therefore a committee of citizens was organized, petitions were circulated, and letters were sent to the governor and a state senator active in water-pollution control. Continued pressure from the citizens, local newspapers, and television finally brought about orders from the state government resulting in the construction of a private treatment facility at one plant and a change of process at the other. This particular source of industrial pollution was brought to an end.

QUESTIONS AND PROJECTS

1. Describe hydrogen bonding and its effect on the properties of water. Name another molecule which might be expected to exhibit hydrogen bonding.

2. Where is the earth's water located? What is the hydrological cycle?

3. Discuss
a. Latent heat of vaporization
b. Polar molecule
c. Limnology
d. Biodegradation
e. BOD

4. How does intermolecular attraction affect the physical state (solid, liquid, or gas) of a chemical?

5. Which water users *need* the most water? Which *lose* the most?

6. Describe methods for (a) providing fresh water (other than pollution control) and (b) conserving fresh water.

7. Estimate how much water an average United States family consumes daily for all purposes. How much for each purpose?

8. How can algae help and hinder in water treatment?

9. A nuclear power plant is discharging large volumes of hot water into an adjacent river. What effect might this have?

10. Discuss a water-pollution problem with which you are personally acquainted. How is the solution to be found?

11. When a liquid evaporates from the palm of your hand, there is a cooling effect. Explain this.

12. Would it take more energy to boil a pound of water or melt a pound of ice? Explain.

13. Find out what water costs in your community. In view of the impending scarcity of water and the huge cost of water treatment and conservation, do you feel this is a reasonable charge? Would increased rates affect personal usage and waste?

14. If weather could be controlled, suggest a method of deciding what the weather should be.

15. Describe a stream's self-purification.

14

AIR POLLUTION

We have just completed a study of water and the importance of its purity and adequacy of supply. We are beginning to realize that we cannot take for granted this priceless commodity. There is another commodity that we also assume is present for our use in unlimited quantity—*clean air.* Essential as water is to our life, we could probably postpone a drink of water or even our lunch. However, we could not very well postpone the next few breaths we must take. We draw about 30 pounds of air into our lungs each day and give very little thought to this automatic but all-important biological process. But why be concerned about the air we breathe? Isn't the atmosphere, which weighs billions of tons, vast enough to supply all of us? Aren't smog problems isolated and confined to certain large industrial urban areas? In answer to these questions, the public has recently begun to realize that clean air is not always available and that it is a general rather than an isolated problem. Air pollution is becoming evident in smaller cities and even in many suburban areas.

◀ PHOTO BY PERMISSION OF *MINNEAPOLIS TRIBUNE.*

The 90 million cars now in use, the ever-expanding number of industrial and power plants, the rapidly growing population, and the sprawling urban areas are creating air-pollution situations which are steadily worsening. There will be a serious threat to our health and economy if steps are not taken now to study and correct existing problems and to prevent the creation of new ones.

SMOG—A NUISANCE OR A HAZARD?

Some shrug off the air pollution problem as merely a discomfiture or an inconvenience, comparing a serious occurrence of smog to a thick fog. It is true that smog and other polluted air conditions with similar names decrease visibility and thus create a nuisance and a hazard. It is also true that there are present in polluted air a variety of simple and complex chemical structures which are known to be extremely hazardous to our health. When one considers the London smog of 1952 which took about 4,000 lives, it becomes frighteningly evident that smog can be more than an inconvenience or unesthetic. In 1962, London had another smog attack which took only a few hundred lives. Presumably, England's emergency efforts to produce clean air after the first tragedy at least improved the previous conditions.

While England has had and continues to have serious air problems, the United States also has many of its own. In Donora, Pennsylvania, a smog developed that lasted four days. Over 7,000 people became sick and 20 people died, compared to only 2 persons during a four-day period in an average year. As in London, the causative agent was presumed to be a mixture of sulfur dioxide, sulfuric acid, and soot. The chief source of this lethal combination was the burning of coal. This, together with a stagnant weather system, produced symptoms such as sore throats, headaches, coughing, nausea, etc. The persons mostly affected in this and other polluted air situations are the young and old.

Los Angeles is afflicted with a different type of smog. In the 1940s this city began to experience a smog which was usually not very long in duration but was very irritating to the eyes and damaging to trees and crops. In contrast to the conditions producing London fog, the weather was generally sunny and dry. The agents causing the ill effects are hydrocarbons chiefly from motor vehicles, nitrogen oxides from motor vehicles and power plants, and an abundance of sunlight which initiates reactions among these chemicals to produce some very harmful structures. Since this smog is not really a combination of smoke and fog and since there are photochemical reactions involved, it is more properly referred to as a photochemical smog. Los Angeles is not alone in having sunshine and an ever-growing number of cars. New York, Detroit, Washington, and many other cities are experiencing smog problems.

The health hazards are many. Obvious results of high exposure are a variety of respiratory disorders such as chronic bronchitis, emphysema, and asthma. Less obvious are possible chronic effects due to continuous exposure to pollutants in lower concentrations. Admittedly, there is a great lack of knowledge of the health effects of pollutants. Some have been shown to cause cancer in animals, and just as with statistical studies on smoking, there has been established a consistent pattern of lung cancer occurrence in relation to exposure to smog.

AND SMOG COSTS MONEY

Add to these serious health problems a few economic ones. For instance, smog areas are usually dirty areas, and cleaning bills for clothes, windows, and even buildings place a drain on the community. Animals can be poisoned, buildings can be damaged, and crops can be spoiled. All these effects on top of the health problem make air pollution a topic of concern for everyone. With the increase in population, cars, and industry, and with the decrease in open spaces, this problem will continue to increase unless we take steps now to protect future generations.

COMPOSITION OF THE ATMOSPHERE

Since it is obvious that the atmosphere is conspiring against us in this problem of smog, we should take a moment to study its composition and movement. We may not be able to control either, but an understanding might allow us to plan better for the future. We mentioned that the atmosphere weighs billions of tons. We also know that about 99.999 percent of the mass of air is within an altitude of 50 miles of the earth. There appears to be enough air here for us to breathe and to hold the impurities. However, mixing takes place only within the first two miles.

Pollutants rarely rise beyond this limit and, in some cases, are restricted to the depth of only a few hundred feet. As a result our air reservoir is not as unlimited as we may have imagined. The air within this two-mile limit is essentially a mixture of nitrogen gas (N_2, about 78 percent) and oxygen gas (O_2, almost 21 percent) with small amounts of argon (A), carbon dioxide (CO_2), water (H_2O), ozone (O_3), helium (He), hydrogen (H_2), methane (CH_4), and other gases. We have already seen how water in the air and in the oceans acts as a heat stabilizer for the earth. In addition, there is normally present in air a certain amount of dust. This also acts as a stabilizer by filtering out part of the sun's rays while performing the very necessary task of acting as nuclei on which raindrops can form. Ozone, at high elevations, does its job, too, by absorbing the sun's strong ultraviolet radiation. Carbon dioxide is also involved in the earth's heat balance. The earth absorbs much of the sun's radiation but reradiates some of the energy as infrared radiation. Carbon dioxide has the property of absorbing this radiation, as do water and ozone.

The concentrations of water and ozone are not influenced to any extent by man's activities; due to the consumption of coal, oil, and gasoline, however, the carbon dioxide content of the air has been on the increase. It is conceivable that a continued increase might bring about melting of the ice caps and consequent flooding of land areas. In addition to the normal components of the air, there are, of course, the many pollutants that we are donating. These will be discussed after a brief consideration of the weather patterns that can cause or cure a smog condition.

AIR MOVEMENT

Air can move vertically or sideways. If prevailing winds are reasonably high, there is little chance for smog formation. Unfortunately for Los Angeles, there is a fairly low annual average windspeed in that area. However, even areas with higher average windspeeds have periods when there is little or no air movement.

The other way in which air mixes and pollutants are carried away is by vertical movement. The earth is warm and air generally gets colder with increasing altitude. The air near the earth, on being heated, expands and rises. If the air into which it rises is cooler and thus more dense, the heated air, which is lighter, will continue to rise. If, on the other hand, the heated air rising from the earth meets still warmer air, it will be heavier than the air above and will sink back down again. This condition, where there is a warm blanket of air covering a colder blanket, is called *inversion*. At night we frequently have a temporary inversion, which dispels in the morning as soon as the sun starts to heat the earth and the air close to the earth. However, in a location that frequently or occasionally has low prevailing winds, air that contains pollutants will develop a smog when an inversion does occur.

The direction and speed of prevailing winds and all other meteorological conditions should be taken into account when planning the location of a smokestack or other source of air pollution. Furthermore, the advice of meteorologists should be sought in predicting weather conditions which may warrant smog alerts. Such weather data can also be used in initiating and maintaining controls on various emissions that might reach harmful levels in certain situations.

THE POLLUTANTS

Exactly what are the various air pollutants and what are their sources? In a metropolitan area there are many pollutants but only four major sources. The latter are motor vehicles, thermoelectric power plants, industries, and householders (who make their contributions by burning fuel and rubbish). The pollutants themselves will be discussed one at a time and will be related where possible to specific sources.

SULFUR DIOXIDE, SO_2, AND SULFURIC ACID, H_2SO_4

Oxides of sulfur, principally sulfur dioxide, are liberated wherever coal and sulfur-containing fuel oil are burned. Other sources include plants that manufacture sulfuric acid and certain operations that involve the smelting of sulfide ores. Most everyone has burned sulfur at one time or another and has smelled or, perhaps more accurately, "tasted" the odor of sulfur dioxide. It is a very acrid bitter-sweet taste that seems to linger in the mouth, nose, and throat. A large dose of the gas will produce extreme irritation to the lungs with a resultant fit of coughing. In the presence of air, sulfur dioxide is converted to sulfur trioxide, another oxide of sulfur.

$$SO_2 \xrightarrow{\text{Oxygen}} SO_3$$

Sulfur dioxide   Sulfur trioxide

This reaction is probably catalyzed (helped along) by various metal oxides that may also be present in the polluted air. On contact with moisture, the sulfur trioxide is rapidly converted to sulfuric acid.

$$SO_3 + H_2O \longrightarrow H_2SO_4$$

Sulfur   Water   Sulfuric
trioxide   acid

Thus, there is produced a fine mist of sulfuric acid which is visible in many areas where these conditions exist. In London, where a great deal of coal burning was taking place, the blame for most of the deaths has been placed chiefly upon the concentrations of sulfur dioxide and sulfuric acid in the stagnant smog.

Of less importance than the human health hazard, but also worthy of note, are the other effects of sulfur dioxide and sulfuric acid. Limestone, marble, roofing slate, and mortar are readily attacked and dissolved by sulfuric acid. All these building materials contain carbonates which react rapidly with acids. (An easy demonstration of the effect of acid on carbonate can be performed in your own kitchen. Pour a little vinegar, which contains acetic acid, onto some baking soda or sodium bicarbonate, and watch the vigorous bubbling that takes place!) Moreover, sulfuric acid will corrode electrical contacts, attack vegetation, deteriorate paper and textiles, and even dissolve nylon hose. The combination of sulfur dioxide and sulfuric acid is one of the worst and most widespread pollutants that man contributes to the air he breathes.

CARBON MONOXIDE, CO

In the United States, millions of tons of carbon monoxide are added each year to the atmosphere. The source is the incomplete combustion of any carbon-containing fuel, primarily the burning of gasoline in motor vehicles. The combustion of a hydrocarbon fuel (gasoline, oil, or natural gas) can be illustrated by considering the combustion of the simplest hydrocarbon, methane, CH_4. When methane is burned completely, that is, when there is enough oxygen available, the reaction produces carbon dioxide, CO_2, and water, H_2O. All the carbon is converted to carbon dioxide, and all the hydrogen is converted to water. However, when there is insufficient oxygen available, the products are carbon monoxide, CO, and water. Notice that a limited amount of oxygen yields an oxide with only one atom of oxygen per carbon atom, whereas an ample oxygen supply yields an oxide with two atoms of oxygen per atom of carbon. There is a great deal of difference between these two oxides. Carbon dioxide, which is a product of our human combustion process, the oxidation of food, is a normal component of our breath. Carbon monoxide, on the other hand, is an insidious and deadly gas. This gas, which is very stable in the atmosphere, is insidious because it is odorless. The toxicity is due to the fact that it ties up the hemoglobin in the blood, thus blocking the normal transport of oxygen from the lungs to the various portions of the body. The action is gradual and the victim usually falls asleep, unaware of what is taking place. Many deaths have occurred in garages where engines have been carelessly left running or in parked vehicles where exhaust fumes may find their way into the car's interior. In addition to the acute effect (high dosage) of carbon monoxide, there may be other low-level effects which could interfere with a motorist's reactions and judgment. Because of the increasing volume of cars on the roads, research in such areas is continuing. It would appear that complete and efficient combustion is the solution to the carbon monoxide problem. However, you will no doubt question whether we are not just contributing to another problem that we have already mentioned—that of too much carbon dioxide in the atmosphere. Remember that there is a possibility that a continued increase in carbon dioxide might lead to an increase in the earth's temperature over a period of several centuries. Later in this chapter we will present possible alternatives to the production of carbon monoxide, carbon dioxide, and other hydrocarbon-combustion pollutants.

OXIDES OF NITROGEN

There are other oxides produced in the combustion of fuel. Unlike carbon oxides, for which the carbon comes from the fuel itself, nitrogen oxides are synthesized mainly from the nitrogen present in the air. There are several oxides of nitrogen, but only two are found in appreciable concentration in polluted air. These are nitric oxide, NO, and nitrogen dioxide, NO_2. Nitric oxide, a colorless gas, is easily converted by the oxygen in the air to brown nitrogen dioxide. The conditions for the formation of nitric oxide are high temperature and high pressure followed by rapid cooling. Thus, the combustions in automobile cylinders and in large electrical power plants are prime sources of this pollutant. If cooling were not rapid, decomposition of the nitric oxide back to harmless nitrogen and oxygen would take place. While both oxides are quite toxic, nitrogen dioxide is by far the more hazardous of the two. In fact, at equivalent levels, it's more harmful than carbon monoxide. Chronic lung conditions and even deaths have been attributed to breathing nitrogen dioxide. It should be noted that smokers are already exposed to a considerable dosage which is present in all tobacco smoke. Another effect of nitrogen oxides, and probably a more serious one, considering the concentrations that generally exist in polluted air, is the part they play in the production of other harmful structures. These reactions, which involve sunlight, oxides of nitrogen, and hydrocarbons, will be discussed next.

PHOTOCHEMICALS

We have all seen clouds of smoke emerging from old cars and even from some not-so-old cars. Some of this cloud is condensing water vapor. (Remember that water is a product of hydrocarbon combustion.) However, much of this cloud may be incompletely burned fuel or lubricating oil that has found its way into the exhaust system. An engine that is operating very poorly will often leave large deposits of soot near the tail pipe exit. All cars, whether we can see it or not, are adding hydrocarbons to the atmosphere at an alarming rate; the total amounts to thousands of tons per day. In addition, other carbon compounds (organics) are being emitted during the refining and handling of petroleum products and from various other industrial sources which dispose of harmful volatile organics by exhausting them into the atmosphere. The reaction of various organics (note that the term hydrocarbon refers to a particular class of organic compounds, those that contain only carbon and hydrogen) with nitrogen oxides in the presence of sunlight produces compounds that irritate the eyes, damage plants, reduce visibility, crack rubber, and probably perform other equally nasty tricks. The process begins with nitrogen dioxide absorbing sunlight in the blue and near-ultraviolet region of the spectrum. The nitrogen dioxide then fairly rapidly decomposes into nitric oxide and atomic oxygen, O. The atomic oxygen in the presence of nitrogen dioxide can react with hydrocarbons, particularly those with double or triple bonds. Ethylene, $CH_2{=}CH_2$, is an example of a hydrocarbon with a reactive double bond. (Remember ethylene from Chaps. 10 and 11 on polymers?) Products of the reaction are complicated-sounding things, such as peroxyacetyl nitrate, a very powerful eye irritant. Another product, resulting from the reaction of atomic oxygen, O, and oxygen molecules, O_2, is ozone, O_3, a highly toxic gas which can produce decreased lung capacity, pulmonary edema, and bronchitis. The ozone has another function in this photochemical smog. It converts nitric oxide back to nitrogen dioxide which is then ready to absorb more light energy and keep things humming along. There are many more reactions involved, some of which are quite complex, and consequently research continues to try to unravel the interwoven relationships. This type of smog is the Los Angeles type and not the London smog with its soot, sulfur dioxide, and sulfuric acid. However, it is quite possible that sulfur dioxide, which can be readily oxidized by ozone to sulfur trioxide, plays a role in the photochemical smog. Some feel that sulfuric acid may help the other pollutants in poisoning man by allowing better penetration into the lung tissues (this is called a synergistic or "helping" effect). Wherever there is a large number of cars (where is there not?) and a supply of sunlight and still, dry air, there is the opportunity for photochemical smog and its deleterious effects. It is up to us to find methods of combating these conditions, which threaten to become worse in years to come. Suggestions for improving the situation will be presented after a discussion of some additional air pollutants.

OTHER AIR POLLUTANTS

RADIOACTIVE CONTAMINANTS

You will recall from Chap. 2 on structure that the nucleus of an atom contains protons and neutrons. Atoms of the same element may contain various numbers of neutrons. These atoms are called *isotopes*. If the nuclei of these isotopes are unstable and undergo decomposition, the isotopes are referred to as *radioactive*. Decomposition or decay of radioactive isotopes produces other isotopes, and during the process nuclear fragments or high intensity radiation similar to x-rays are emitted. (In addition, enormous amounts of energy can in some cases be released, as will be further discussed in Chap. 16 on nuclear energy.) Such fragments and radiation, which can cause any number of known and unknown reactions to take place, are harmful to living organisms. The manner in which they are harmful is not well understood, and most of our evidence is only statistical. The effects may take a generation or two to become clear. In the meantime, it may be too late to stop the damage that has already been caused by radioactive pollution. There is a certain small amount of such pollution that occurs naturally, both from soils and rocks that emit radioactive gases and from cosmic irradiation of gases in the air. We have always lived with this level of natural radioactivity, which apparently has no ill effect. However, within recent years, due to the increased application of nuclear energy, man's contribution to atmospheric radioactivity has increased, and it will certainly increase further if we do not insist upon strict controls. The chief source is atmospheric testing of atomic weapons, which at present is under a worldwide suspension. Other sources include the preparation, use, and refining of fuel for nuclear reactors; the use of radioactive isotopes in research, industry, and medicine; and the use of nuclear energy to replace conventional propellants in spacecraft.

AGRICULTURAL CHEMICALS

The insecticides, herbicides, fungicides, etc., that were described in Chaps. 9 and 12 present a problem of contamination not only to our water but also to the air. Some of these poisons are extremely toxic, and some are very resistant to atmospheric decomposition. Real hazards exist, and people should be aware of them. How many householders carelessly spray insecticides indoors or in closed areas? Continued breathing of some of these products, regardless of the perfumes that mask them, can produce serious harm. In particular, the insecticide parathion, which has accidentally taken a number of lives, must be stored and handled with utmost care. Unfortunately, many people do not take time to read labels and feel that anything they can purchase in a pretty package certainly should not be very dangerous. *Caveat emptor*—let the buyer beware! Air contamination with agricultural chemicals can take place during aerial dusting of crops, ground spraying and dusting of crops, public treatment of parks and forests, and garden spraying by individual householders.

HYDROCARBONS WHICH CAN PRODUCE CANCER

Certain hydrocarbon structures, which are capable of producing cancer in animals, have been found in polluted atmospheres. These structures are for the most part large ring systems, consisting usually of four, five, or six 6-membered rings of carbon atoms stuck together. A typical carcinogen is benzopyrene, which, incidentally, is also found in cigarette smoke. These harmful hydrocarbon structures are found wherever there is incomplete combustion of organic matter, as in gasoline and diesel oil, incinerators, and refuse burning on open dumps. The total contribution of pollutants to the production of cancer is difficult to pinpoint and may be a relatively small one, compared to cigarette smoking and industrial exposures. However, statistical data indicate that there is a relationship. For instance, British citizens, who had been exposed for years to the coal-burning smogs and who immigrated to South Africa or New Zealand, had a much higher lung cancer incidence than the natives who were very heavy smokers. It has also been shown that the incidence of lung cancer is higher in metropolitan areas than in rural areas. Certainly, any possibility of harm should be eliminated from the atmosphere as fast as possible.

SOOT

At first thought, it would appear that soot is nothing but a dirty nuisance. Unfortunately, it is more of a problem than that. Soot is an intricate network of carbon atoms which has a very large and absorbent surface area. The absorbing power of charcoal is well known; charcoal is widely used in gas masks to trap various harmful gases. The soot, which arises generally from incomplete combustion of fuel, absorbs hydrocarbons that are not completely burned. Some of these hydrocarbons are, as we have just seen, quite harmful. Furthermore, soot can act like sulfuric acid mist in that it seems to be efficient in penetrating deeply into the lungs, carrying along the other harmful pollutants. Since soot is an easy pollutant to detect, it should be one of the first to be prevented or eliminated.

OTHER POLLUTANTS

Other pollutants which are either found in very small concentration or found only in certain industrial locations are hydrogen sulfide gas, fluorides, and lead, the last mostly from gasoline containing tetraethyl lead and tetramethyl lead. It is interesting to note that studies have demonstrated a higher lead level in the blood of smokers than of non-smokers who live in the same areas. Many years ago lead arsenate spray was used on tobacco in the United States. Apparently, the soil became so contaminated that successive plantings continued to absorb the lead even though the spray was discontinued. This demonstrates the persistency that is often an undesirable property of a pesticide.

TECHNICAL SOLUTIONS

Having considered the various atmospheric pollutants and their sources, we should logically consider the possible technical and political avenues to the correction of existing problems and the prevention of future ones. Can smog be removed? Many suggestions have been made, but so far none are technically feasible. Ideas such as blowing the air away with great fans, enclosing highways in tunnels, sucking the air into sewer systems, and focusing mirrors on a spot in the atmosphere to create air current, are either unworkable or economically unfeasible. Since we cannot remove the smog, the only practical solution—one which reminds us of the water problem—is to prevent the problem from occurring. Soot, ash, and other particles can be removed with electrostatic and cyclone precipitators. Electrostatic precipitators put a charge on the particles which then settle out on an oppositely charged plate, whereas cyclone precipitators spin the air about and force the particles against an outer wall where they settle and are collected. Other devices, such as baghouses and settling tanks, are being employed for capturing exhaust particles and gases.

Incomplete combustion, which gives rise to harmful hydrocarbons, can be prevented by designing more efficient furnaces and engines and by installing units on motor vehicles to burn any unused hydrocarbons. Prohibition of open burning of waste has been instituted and may become more generally necessary. If low-cost methods cannot be found for removing sulfur dioxide from smokestack gases, then fuels containing sulfur may have to be limited. The coal and heavy oil used in ships, factories, and power plants contain large amounts of sulfur. Conversion to natural gas, which contains very little sulfur, may be required where this gas is available. Since the number of cars continues to increase at a rapid rate and since urban areas are becoming more and more congested, much thought should be given to new methods of mass transportation. If really good transportation were available from the suburbs to the urban working areas, persons would be willing to abandon the daily driving and parking problems. Another attack on the problem—apparently reactionary but really progressive—is the study of the replacement of gasoline engine automobiles with electrically powered cars. If the automotive industry diverted a large portion of its research potential toward this goal, a realistic solution might be forthcoming. Add to this the possibility of the return to electric streetcars and electric buses (which probably should never have been allowed to disappear in the first place).

Other replacements of conventional sources of energy are being investigated. Tidal, solar, and nuclear energies will no doubt gradually replace the use of fossil fuel, which in any case will eventually become depleted at the rate we are consuming it. There are then technical solutions either presently or potentially available. How do we apply them? As with water-pollution problems, there are some conscientious industries and munici-palities that are willing and anxious to do their part. On the other hand,

FIGURE 14–1   A PROTOTYPE ELECTRIC CAR, POWERED WITH LITHIUM-NICKEL-FLUORIDE BATTERIES (FOREGROUND). THE "PASSENGER" COSTS EXTRA. (BY PERMISSION OF AUTOMOBILE MANUFACTURERS ASSOCIATION, INC.)

there are many, including a large percentage of the disinterested public, who want to do nothing. In particular, they do not want to face the problem, and above all, they do not want to spend any time or money in correcting it. The first step in changing such a situation is to alert and educate the general public. The next is to get the cooperation of the federal, state, and local governments in setting criteria for air purity, in providing funds for determining technical solutions, and in providing funds for developing and maintaining air-control programs.

GOVERNMENTAL REGULATION

Many cities in addition to Los Angeles have been experiencing air-pollution problems. More and more people are beginning to realize the hazards that are currently involved and that threaten to worsen. As a result, action at the local, state, and federal levels has been on the increase. The Federal Clean Air Act of 1963 gave a great impetus to corrective action. The Public Health Service Division of Air Pollution has been responsible for the program. In January, 1967, this division was reorganized and renamed the National Center for Air Pollution Control. Amendments to the Clean Air Act have given the Center the power to award grants for research on the development and main-tenance of control programs to correct interstate, intrastate, and (if other countries will grant reciprocal rights) international air-pollution problems. A significant step toward arresting air pollution from motor vehicles was made possible by the 1965 and 1966 amendments to the Clean Air Act. Standards have been adopted for all gasoline-powered passenger cars and light trucks, including imported vehicles. Starting with the 1968 models, all hydrocarbon emissions from the crankcase must be eliminated, and hydrocarbon and carbon monoxide emission from the exhaust system must be reduced. It is believed that this will result in an overall reduction of about 50 percent in carbon monoxide emission and about 60 percent in hydrocarbon emission. As the num-ber of cars increases, even this measure of improvement may be offset and the standards may have to be tightened. There are still further problems in connection with motor vehicles. Gasoline evaporates from the gas tank and carburetor, thus adding to the hydrocarbon content of the air. In addition, there have as yet been no standards set for diesel engines or for nitrogen oxides. As research comes up with more solu-tions in all areas of air pollution, so must these solutions be applied to the problems at hand.

QUESTIONS AND PROJECTS

1. Why is our air reservoir not as large as it might appear? What is the composition of air?

2. In the atmosphere, what is the function of each of the following:
a. Moisture
b. Dust
c. Ozone
d. Carbon dioxide

3. Why might an increase in carbon dioxide be a hazard in the future?

4. Discuss
a. Inversion
b. Smog
c. Photochemical smog
d. Isotopes

5. Write the balanced equation for the reaction of (a) methane and oxygen to yield carbon monoxide and water and (b) methane and oxygen to yield carbon dioxide and water. What condition favors equation (a) over equation (b)?

6. Draw a diagram to illustrate the photochemical smog process.

7. Devise a simple experiment which can measure the amount of soot in the air in your neighborhood.

8. Why is soot harmful? How is it eliminated industrially?

9. Describe the pollution devices on your car or on a friend's car.

10. Discuss a special air-pollution problem in your town or area. How can this problem be solved?

11. Compare the London smog with the Los Angeles smog.

12. Give a list of common air pollutants. Comment on each.

13. Report on the film on air pollution. What was its message?

14. How can a meteorologist help in the battle on air pollution?

15. What are the major sources of air pollution and how can they be prevented?

15

HOUSEHOLD
CHEMICAL
PRODUCTS

We have now studied a number of areas in which chemical principles and their application play a very significant role. Certainly our basic understanding of matter and its properties is important when we are concerned with such matters as providing clean air and water for ourselves and our descendants. But even in our own homes chemical knowledge is of direct value. All of us, every day, use at least several household chemical preparations. These products, which are available in supermarkets, in drugstores, in department stores, and from door-to-door salesmen, cover a very wide spectrum of chemical content and useful application. Detergents, bleaches, disinfectants, waxes, deodorants, insecticides, oven cleaners, rat killers, paints, and spot removers are just a few of the hundreds of chemical products in use in the home today. Some of these have been in use for years, but many are of recent development. Some are fairly harmless to man and animals, and others are extremely hazardous. In any event, the average household spends approximately 30 percent of the grocery bill each week on various chemical products, and if for no other reason, each of us should have some knowledge of the types of raw materials involved, how the products perform their jobs, and the precautions to be taken with certain products. It will also be interesting to consider for typical formulations the cost of the product, including packaging and labeling, to reveal the amount of profit involved.

It must be pointed out that there are many companies, both large and small, involved in the manufacture and sale of chemical household products. The general assumption is that a particular detergent, say, is patented and therefore is unique. Sometimes this is the case, but more often the formulation is a trade secret (which is usually not so secret), and the product is unique only in that it has a special trademark. Thus, there are numerous products which are extremely similar in composition but which vie for sales through the attractiveness of the container, the cleverness of the name, and the effectiveness of the television, newspaper, radio, and store promotion. Fortunately for the producer, but perhaps unfortunately for the buyer, the profits are generally high enough to allow for extensive advertising. On the other hand, the products available to us today provide a more healthy and more convenient way of life. None of us would want to do away with the conveniences we now enjoy, and indeed, some part of the profit that we pay chemical producers does support continuing research. This research develops new and useful products for our benefit.

Of all the household chemical products, the largest volume is probably made up by the detergents and related cleaners. Consequently, we shall first look into the laundry products, dishwashing compounds, and special cleaners, followed by a consideration of a random selection of other common items.

LAUNDRY PRODUCTS

SOAP

Soap, which is a product of fat and a base such as sodium hydroxide, NaOH, used to be the chief laundry detergent. However, the large number and variety of synthetic detergents has long since displaced soap as the leader in this field. (Please note that both soap and synthetic detergents produce detergency. The exact terminology should be soap versus nonsoap.) Nevertheless, soap still possesses many desirable properties; it remains the principle agent for cleaning hands and also maintains a fair share of the laundry market.

MANUFACTURE OF SOAP

Fats and oils are long-chain esters. An ester, as you will recall, is a combination of an acid and an alcohol:

$$R-\overset{\displaystyle O}{\overset{\|}{C}}-OH \quad HO-B \longrightarrow R-\overset{\displaystyle O}{\overset{\|}{C}}-O-B$$

Acid   Alcohol   An ester

In this case, the alcohol is glycerine and the acids are various long-chain hydrocarbon acids such as stearic acid:

Glycerine   Stearic acid   Fat
(a glyceride)

The fats are solids, while the oils are liquids. Both animal and vegetable fats and oils can be employed in the manufacture of soap. The reaction involves the treatment of the fat with sodium hydroxide, with a resultant splitting of the fat into glycerine and the sodium salt of the corresponding acid. Such a reaction is called *saponification*.

Glyceride   Sodium   Glycerine   Soap
hydroxide   (sodium stearate)

Notice that the soap is merely the sodium salt of the long-chain acid. In the example given above, the salt is sodium stearate.

SOAP PROPERTIES

How does such an awkward-looking structure perform the cleaning tasks that it does? If we try to use water alone for removing dirt, say from clothing, we find it remarkably ineffective. You might knock off a few large clumps of soil, but the rest is not attracted to water, does not dissolve or disperse in the water, and indeed has nothing to do with the water. From the water's point of view this is perfectly satisfactory, for the water molecules are attracted to each other and have no desire to keep company with dirt, grease, oil, or what-have-you. When small amounts of soap are added to water, we find that groups of soap molecules clump together. Looking back at the formula for soap, you will observe that there is a salt end of the soap ion and a hydrocarbon end.

$$^-O-\overset{\overset{\displaystyle O}{\|}}{C}-(CH_2)_{16}-CH_3$$

Salt end
dissolves in water
(hydrophilic)

Hydrocarbon end
dissolves in oil
(hydrophobic)

Recalling that the water molecule is polar, with a positive and a negative end, we understand why the negatively charged salt end is attracted to, and therefore soluble in, water. On the contrary, the hydrocarbon end, which is nonpolar and whose carbon-hydrogen structure is similar to that of oil and grease, is not attracted to water. The technical terms for the two ends are *hydrophilic* (water-loving) and *hydrophobic* (water-fearing). The result is that groups of soap ions clump together in ball-like shapes with their hydrocarbon ends toward the center and the salt end toward the water. The water-insoluble portions are shielded from the water by the water-soluble portions, thus preventing the soap from separating out of solution. At the surface of some oil, the hydrophobic portion is attracted to the oil, while the hydrophilic end is attracted to the water. Hence we are bringing about a bond between the oil and the water. With sufficient agitation, the oil can be broken up into tiny droplets and dispersed throughout the water. We have broken down the water's surface tension, which is the force holding the molecules of the water together.

SURFACE-ACTIVE AGENTS

An agent which can affect surface tension is called a surface-active agent—*surfactant*, for short. Likewise, any material which can disperse something in another medium is called a *dispersing agent*. While we are throwing terms about, we may as well learn a few more. If you dropped a greasy rag into pure water, you know you would observe the water practically recoil from the dirty surface. A substance such as soap, which breaks down this repulsion and allows the liquid to wet the surface, is called—you guessed it—a *wetting agent*. The opposite situation can be purposely brought about by treating a fabric with a very hydrophobic material to make it water-repellent. If oil is agitated with water containing a surfactant, the tiny oil droplets are dispersed throughout the water medium. This product is called an *emulsion*, and the surfactant in this case is an *emulsifying agent*. Cake dough is an oil-in-water emulsion in which fat particles are dispersed in a continuous watery phase, whereas butter is a water-in-oil emulsion wherein water droplets are dispersed in a continuous phase of fat. If particles of dirt can be suspended in water so that they do not drop out, the agent responsible is called a *suspending agent*. The process of foaming is brought about by surface-active agents. At the surface of a soap solution the hydrophobic ends aim up toward the air, trying to get away from the water, while the hydrophilic ends stick down into the solution. This results in a lowering of the surface tension with foaming as a result. It has been found, however, that foaming is not a necessary part of detergent action. Structures have been developed which minimize foaming, and for structures that foam excessively there are additives available to suppress the foaming action.

DETERGENCY

We have met with a number of processes and a large number of terms. Most of us are just interested in whether something will clean or not. Of course, the chemist wants to know in detail what is going on in the cleaning process so that he may design better products. The entire detergency process is still not a clear one. The various actions, such as wetting, dispersing, emulsification, and suspension, are probably all involved to some extent. In any event, the basic principles that we have learned from the example of soap can be applied to all detergent operations. In fact, all detergents, soaps, and nonsoaps are really quite similar. They have a structure with water-loving end and water-fearing ends.

FIGURE 15–1   SOLID PARTICLES TREATED WITH A SURFACTANT ARE FLOATED
AWAY. (*COURTESY OF H. R. SPEDDEN.*)

There is a delicate balance between the strengths of these two properties. By varying the types of ends and the lengths of ends, one can obtain a large series of surfactants with varying properties. Some might be more effective as wetting agents, some as emulsifying agents. They are all surfactants, and it is usually their final end use which classifies them.

COLLOIDS

Before we leave the theoretical aspects of detergency, we should say something about the type of solution which the soap and other detergents form. Such solutions belong to a class known as *colloids.*

A soap solution is not what we call a true solution. In a true solution, we have simple molecules and ions. The clumps of ions (called micelles) in the soap solution are quite large by comparison. This can easily be demonstrated. A membrane with very tiny pores will allow the passage of ordinary ions but will hold back the much larger micelles. In addition, a beam of light passes unseen through an ordinary solution, but with a colloidal solution, the beam can be seen going right through the solution. The reason for this is that the colloidal particles are large enough (in comparison with the wavelength of visible light) to reflect the light toward our eyes. A similar situation occurs when we observe a ray of sunlight as it reflects from dust particles suspended in the air. Why don't these relatively large soap micelles bump together, collect, and settle to the bottom of the container? Remember that the negatively charged ends of the molecules in the micelles are pointing toward the water. The micelles can be thought of as spheres over which is spread a negative charge. This charge can attract a layer of opposite ions, and in turn, this layer (primary) can attract another layer (secondary). The end result is that we have micelles floating about with electrical charge spread out over their surface. Since the charges are the same, the clumps are repelled and hence do not come together (coagulate). One way to destroy a colloidal system is to add a large number of highly charged ions (for instance, $AlCl_3$, aluminum chloride, or sodium sulfate, Na_2SO_4). Positively charged ions neutralize the charge on negative colloids, and negatively charged ions neutralize the charge on positive colloids. Mutual repulsion is thus eliminated and coagulation commences. Oil and dirt are suspended in solution with the aid of surfactants by the same sort of mechanism. The dirt is surrounded by the detergent which

FIGURE 15–2   MAPLE SAP (*LEFT JAR*) IS COLLOIDAL AND SCATTERS LIGHT; SUGAR WATER (*RIGHT JAR*) IS MOLECULAR AND DOES NOT SCATTER LIGHT. (*COURTESY OF B. M. SHAUB.*)

aims its hydrophobic end toward the dirt and hydrophilic end toward the water. We have a micelle with a dirt particle or oil droplet trapped inside. The charged surface again prevents coagulation. Keep in mind that whatever we have said in principle about the soap ion is also true for the synthetic detergent materials. As we will see, some of the synthetics are ionic, as soap is, while some are nonionic. In the latter case, the hydrophilic end is not ionic but is distinctly polar in nature so that it has an attraction for water molecules. In the micelles these polar ends stick out toward the water and attract ions just as the soap ions do.

SOAP FORMULATIONS

For laundering, soap is not used in the pure state as it is in hand soap. Laundry has a certain amount of natural acidity and can therefore convert the soap back into the original acid.

$$^-O{-}\underset{\substack{\| \\ C}}{\overset{O}{}}{-}(CH_2)_{16}{-}CH_3 \; + \; H^+ \longrightarrow HO{-}\underset{\substack{\| \\ C}}{\overset{O}{}}{-}(CH_2)_{16}{-}CH_3$$

Soap ion   Hydrogen ion   Stearic acid
                            from an acid

Thus, without the soap ion, we have no hydrophilic end and consequently no surfactant. To offset this, various inorganic alkaline compounds that react with acids, such as carbonates, silicates, and phosphates, are added to laundry soap formulations. Not only do these
alkalis neutralize any nasty acids hanging around, but it is found that
the soap does a better job in their presence. However, soap has one big
drawback. Being an anion it does attract cations, and some of the
resultant salts, as opposed to the sodium salt, are quite *in*soluble. Many
water supplies are hard, which means that there is considerable mineral
content, such as calcium, magnesium, and iron. The predominant cul-
prits are calcium and magnesium, whose ions precipitate soap producing a very unpleasant and hard-to-remove scum. Some additives,
particularly certain phosphates, have the job of "tying up" these bad
ions to prevent them from reacting with the soap. But success with such
additives is only partial so that the use of soap products in hard-water
areas is not too desirable. Synthetic detergents, on the other hand, do
not react with hard water and yet do perform their cleaning tasks in
good fashion. (Additives such as those just described, which help or
add to the detergency of the main ingredient, are commonly called
builders.)

SYNTHETIC DETERGENTS

Synthetic detergents or nonsoaps can be classified into three main
groups—cationic, anionic, and nonionic. Let us emphasize again that
the main feature of any surfactant is that it contains hydrophilic and
hydrophobic portions.

CATIONICS

A cationic surfactant, as the name implies, is a positively charged ion,
a cation; and, as you can guess, the cation end of the molecule is the
hydrophilic end.

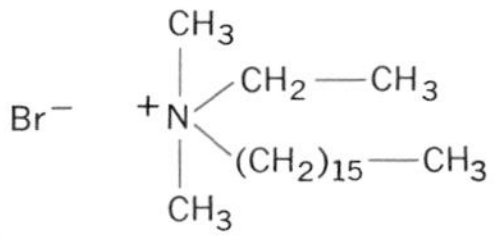

$$CH_3$$

$$Br^- \quad {}^+N \overset{CH_3}{\underset{CH_3}{\overset{\diagup CH_2-CH_3}{\diagdown (CH_2)_{15}-CH_3}}}$$

Cationic surfactant

Cetyl dimethylethyl ammonium bromide
A quaternary ammonium salt

The structure will seem simpler if we compare it with ammonium bromide.

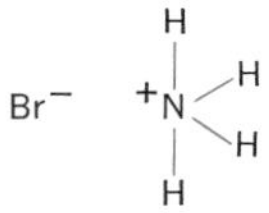

$$Br^- \quad {}^+N \overset{H}{\underset{H}{\overset{\diagup H}{\diagdown H}}}$$

Ammonium bromide

If we replace all the hydrogens with hydrocarbon groups, one of which is a long-chain hydrophobic group, we have a salt similar in structure to ammonium bromide. Since there are four hydrocarbon groups attached to the nitrogen, this compound belongs to a large class called *quaternary ammonium compounds* and sometimes nicknamed "quats." Such surfactants find very special application. They are generally bactericidal and function as the chief ingredient of modern disinfectants. Moreover, some members of this class have the property of adhering to the fabric and giving it a soft "feel." These are the *fabric softeners*.

ANIONICS

Anionics are of course anions, as soap is. The ionic end is very often a sulfate group, $-OSO_3^=$, or a sulfonate group, $-SO_3^=$. The hydrophobic portion can be a straight-chain hydrocarbon, as in soap, or a combination of straight-chain and cyclic hydrocarbon groupings (generally from petroleum). An example of an anionic surfactant is

$$CH_3-(CH_2)_{11}-O-SO_3^- \quad Na^+$$

Lauryl sulfate

This type of anionic is frequently used in hair shampoos. It should be noted that cationics and anionics are usually incompatible, generally producing insoluble products.

NONIONICS

There are surfactants which are not ionic but do have polar and nonpolar portions in their structure. For example,

$$CH_3—(CH_2)_8—C_6H_4—(OCH_2CH_2)_{10}—OCH_2CH_3$$

Here the C_6H_4 is a ring of six carbon atoms known as a benzene ring. Obviously the end of the molecule containing the oxygen atoms is the hydrophilic portion. Recall that the problem of biodegradability was overcome by providing a straight chain (hydrocarbon), as above, rather than a branched one, which is indigestible to the organisms that decompose waste.

DETERGENT ADDITIVES

We might spend a moment on an interesting ingredient that is added to most formulations. This is a product called sodium carboxymethylcellulose (CMC), a water-soluble derivative of cellulose. There is a story that goes with this unusual compound. Immediately after World War II American scientists, sent to Germany, obtained samples of this material, which was supposed to have something to do with detergency. The samples were tested for ordinary detergency by many competent research departments in the United States before someone concluded that the material was not an ordinary detergent at all but a marvelous suspending agent. To demonstrate its ability, one could prepare two large vertical tubes, one filled with pure water and the other with a dilute (0.3 to 1 percent) solution of CMC. A bag of dirt is dumped into each tube, and the mixture is stirred and allowed to settle. In the tube with the plain water, practically complete settling takes place quickly, whereas in the CMC tube suspension is almost indefinite. Thus, the detergent can remove dirt from clothing, but the additive CMC keeps the dirt in suspension and prevents it from redepositing on the clothes. Another additive that is of interest is the sunlight ingredient, the agent which makes clothes whiter and brighter than new. This is nothing but a special dye that has the property of absorbing some of the invisible ultraviolet light from the sun and reemitting it as visible light. We therefore see more light coming back from our newly washed shirt or pillowcase. It may not be cleaner—just brighter. Still another additive is a bleach of one sort or another. Both chlorine and boron compounds are commonly included in formulations to oxidize stubborn stains to colorless products. Many householders prefer to add their own bleach, and therefore sales of liquid and powdered bleaches occupy a big portion of the market. Liquid bleach is a dilute solution (about 5 percent) of sodium hypochlorite. In a gallon of liquid bleach (which weighs about 8 pounds), there is less than half a pound of this inexpensive compound. The buyer is paying mostly for water and the container.

LIQUID LAUNDRY DETERGENTS

Before we leave the field of laundry detergents, we should mention the liquid products. If a truly efficient liquid laundry detergent can be developed, it will probably command great sales. This is so because of the ease of measuring and dispensing, especially since automatic metering devices could be installed on washing machines. Such devices would free the housewife from the mess and bother of handling the detergent (except for occasional refilling of the reservoir). In addition, automatic metering would probably be more saving with the detergent. However, a great problem facing the liquids is solubility. Every substance has a limited solubility, so that the proper ingredients and mixture of ingredients must be found which will have enough water solubility to be as effective as the powdered products. The automatic measuring feature is also provided by solid formulations in the form of compressed cakes. These are convenient to handle and measurement is reduced to counting.

DISHWASHING DETERGENTS

MACHINE PRODUCTS

This application, which sends tons of detergents down the kitchen drain daily, is second only to the laundry usage. There are two main types to consider—hand and machine products. Dishwashing machines are not as delicate as milady's hands and can therefore stand more potent chemicals and higher temperatures. Here the chief ingredients are alkaline inorganics, such as the carbonates, silicates, and phosphates. Some products include a detergent that is stable enough to resist the very strong alkaline medium. If this detergent produces too much foam, it may, just as in automatic clothes washers, prevent the circulation of water through the pump. High enough temperatures are attained in both commercial and home units to produce complete sterilization. In the commercial dishwashing process an after-rinse containing a small amount of surfactant is often employed to prevent spotting of dishes and utensils. The principle involved is to allow any final droplets left to run together in a thin uniform sheet. Then, any minerals or other material that might be in the droplets will not be deposited as small spots but rather will be spread out as an even, invisible film. The amount of surfactant left on the table ware is said to be harmless.

HAND PRODUCTS

Washing dishes by hand requires a much milder medium and, naturally, much lower temperature. The hand dishwashing products, both liquid and solids, generally contain anionics or nonionics combined with various dyes and perfumes. The compositions usually run about 10 to 15 percent "active," which means that the surfactant comprises 10 to 15 percent of the weight of the entire product. The remainder is essentially water. Even in commercial establishments some washing must be done by hand. For instance, where there is a very quick turnover of glasses, as in the local bar, the speed of hand washing is preferred. Disinfecting becomes very important and necessary here, and chemical means must be employed. An old standby is a solution of ordinary chlorine bleach, which is a very effective bactericide. However, the odor and sometimes lingering taste are undesirable, and more recently developed compounds have consequently come into use. These are the *iodophors* and the quaternary compounds. You are familiar with iodophor as the ingredient of "painless iodine." The old-fashioned iodine was just a solution of iodine, I_2 (like hydrogen, H_2, a diatomic molecule), in alcohol. Iodine is not very soluble in water, and thus alcohol, which was probably responsible for most of the zippy sensation, was used as a solvent. Now we have polymers (e.g., polyvinyl pyrollidone) which complex (tie up) iodine molecules and dissolve in water. The resultant solution is a very efficient and painless disinfectant. Another type of disinfectant is the family of quaternary compounds described before. Certain members of this family in the form of a dilute water solution make excellent disinfectants. Of course, disinfecting dishware with iodophors and quats is only one of a great many uses for these excellent products.

CARE WITH DISINFECTANTS

Care must be exercised with these, as with all other chemicals. The very active quaternary compounds, especially, are quite toxic. In one particular bar, the proprietor was in the habit of measuring out his quaternary concentrate in an ordinary bar glass just prior to pouring it into his rinse tank. An unfortunate chap, who probably could not tell one glass from another at the time, picked up the filled measuring glass and took his last drink. Another story about quats involves the lady who injected some into her husband's chocolates. Her sweet plan worked smoothly except that she was caught.

Lest anyone become terrified of products containing quaternary compounds, let me point out that generally we are dealing with fairly dilute solutions. It is the pure materials or concentrated solutions of these that require special care. Remember, also, that almost anything in the wrong concentration can be harmful.

Attempts have been made to produce a liquid product that will be satisfactory both for hand dishwashing and machine laundering. The formulation of a product that is mild enough and yet strong enough is not an easy proposition. Add to this the problem of dissolving a high enough concentration of ingredients in water and we have a doubly difficult matter. Research in this area continues.

OTHER CLEANERS

There are many other types of cleaners available for home use. There are cleaners for rugs, floors, walls, toilet bowls, greasy ovens, paintbrushes, white sidewalls, drains, windows, dogs, etc. There are solutions, emulsions, soluble powders, abrasives, squeeze bottles, aerosols, sponge applicators, dissolvable containers, bars, and creams. You can probably find a cleaner in any kind of package for any kind of special application that you specify. If there is a market for a product, there will be a supplier. We cannot go into all the various items but shall consider a few of the common ones.

RUG SHAMPOOS

Rug shampoos are solutions of nonionics or anionics, very similar to hand dishwashing products, but with a higher active concentration. Professional rug and upholstery cleaners apply such a product with a brush machine and then remove the excess detergent and emulsified grease with a wet vacuum pickup. Metal runners on furniture legs are separated from carpets during drying by means of small pieces of cardboard. Excellent results are attained even though complete penetration is not effected. Carbon tetrachloride and other chlorinated hydrocarbons, such as perchloroethylene, are used in a number of rug products as well as in other applications. Such chemicals act as a direct solvent for grease rather than as a surfactant. They are very effective grease dissolvers, but unfortunately, these chlorinated solvents, particularly "carbon tet," are very toxic compounds. They act in a cumulative way, concentrating mainly in the liver. This is where paying attention to small print on labels is very important. There should be plenty of ventilation available if such products are to be used.

WINDOW CLEANERS

A common glass cleaner is a dilute solution of detergent in isopropyl alcohol (rubbing alcohol) and water. This is a very inexpensive and useful formulation which can be squirted or sprayed directly onto the glass surface. Some cleaners are suspensions which leave an abrasive powder behind as the solvent evaporates. The powder not only helps with the cleaning but clearly shows the spots that are missed. It is also quite useful for making window designs at Christmas time.

OVEN CLEANERS

Women rarely enjoy the task of removing the built-up grease and charcoal that bakes onto the surfaces of an oven. Simple washing with an ordinary detergent is practically a waste of time. Very strong alkali which can attack grease (in much the same way that sodium hydroxide splits oil to make soap and glycerine) appears to be the only efficient chemical solution. Consequently the preparations, which are essentially pure sodium hydroxide (also called lye), carry very stern warnings. Pure lye can cause blindness and can severely burn the skin. As a result, rubber gloves and other precautionary measures must be observed. A complication arises because stove manufacturers, in the interest of economy, are replacing chrome trim with aluminum. Sodium hydroxide attacks aluminum about as readily as acid attacks most metals, and in cleaning an oven it is very difficult to keep the cleaner off the trim. There is a frenzy of research to try to find a chemical combination that will be strong enough to remove the grease but will not destroy the aluminum. A new development which may eliminate this problem, as well as some profits for the chemical producers, is a special heater which produces very high temperatures within the oven for a short period of time. This extreme heat removes the organic matter through oxidation, thus eliminating the need for manual labor.

DRAIN CLEANERS

Just as sodium hydroxide is effective in cutting the grease in an oven, so also is it effective in dirty drains. Since drains can have some pretty resistant blobs of goo, an extra jolt is needed for dislodgement and dissolving. To effect this, bits of aluminum metal are included with the sodium hydroxide. When the product is placed in the drain and water is added, the sodium hydroxide dissolves and reacts violently with the aluminum. The reaction provides hydrogen gas for agitation and plenty of heat to accelerate the action of the lye on the grease. One thing to keep in mind with a drain cleaner is to avoid its use when the drain is completely clogged. If it is used and becomes trapped, the plumber stands a good chance of getting burned when he is summoned to clean out the pipes mechanically.

TOILET BOWL CLEANERS

While lye is used for cleaning the oven and the drains, acid is used to clean a stained toilet. Such stains are a very bad problem in areas that have water with a high iron content. The iron is deposited on the porcelain surface as an oxide, similar to rust. Since rust reacts readily with acids (remember the steel mills that clean their rusty iron parts with acids), products that contain or liberate acid are employed. Commercial products are often strong solutions of hydrochloric acid. For household jobs, acid salts such as sodium acid sulfate are frequently used. Since toilet-bowl cleaning is a rather unsavory task, efforts have been made to make the process as simple as possible. One product features individual packets in which the material is sealed up in a plastic film of polyvinyl alcohol. This polymer has the unusual property of dissolving in water, so that the packet need only be dropped into the toilet and allowed to perform its task. Of course, a little action with a brush or sponge helps a lot.

ALL-PURPOSE CLEANERS

Since there are so many different tasks that cleaners must perform, it becomes immediately obvious that a single, all-purpose cleaner would be desirable. Indeed, there are many compositions, both liquid and solid, which can perform a large number of tasks. The formulations are quite similar to one another, containing a certain amount of nonionic or anionic with various builders. One of the earliest all-purpose liquids, still popular, is an emulsion of refined kerosene in water. It is a waxy-looking liquid with a rather "heavy" odor. The kerosene tends to dissolve hydrophobic materials, such as grease and oil, while the water handles the water-soluble stains. It was developed by a dry cleaner who was always intrigued with the problem of removing oil-soluble and water-soluble spots from clothing. The emulsion, in which the kerosene molecules are dispersed and stabilized by a small amount of surfactant, performs simultaneously the tasks that previously had to be done separately. Ordinary solutions of surfactants do just as good a job and generally present a more acceptable appearance and odor.

ABRASIVE CLEANERS

When all-purpose cleaners run into particularly stubborn stains, assistance is available from abrasive cleaners. These are powders that owe their success to their grinding action. Bad sink stains, very dirty walls or floors, and grimy hands are popular targets for these cleaners. The abrasive ingredient may be finely powdered feldspar or silica. A small amount of soap, builder, dye, perfume, and bleach is generally included in the formula. Inasmuch as these products do their work by mechanical abrasion of the surfaces involved, care must be taken that certain surfaces do not become permanently scratched.

OTHER PRODUCTS

There are far more chemical household products than we have discussed. There are hair products, deodorants, paints, shaving cream, insecticides, air fresheners, polishes, waxes, and many, many more. It would take quite a few chapters to describe all the products which we use every day in and around the home. Many of the principles we have learned in the study of the cleaning compounds apply equally well in the related areas. Many different trade names often have extremely similar formulations, which are in themselves fairly uncomplicated. It should be pointed out that products that are to be used directly in or on the body come under the regulations of the Food, Drug and Cosmetic Act. Approval for use of such an item must be granted by the FDA. This measure is important since it provides protection to the consumer. There are many compounds that will perform certain personal jobs quite well but which are harmful in some way to the human body. For instance, a new product that has just become popular is a hot shaving cream in an aerosol can. In the nozzle where the propellant begins to expand with the shaving cream composition to make a foam, a second compartment delivers a small amount of material which will liberate heat on contact with the foam. Many chemicals are capable of liberating heat on contact with water, but most of them are injurious to the skin. However, a material which is acceptable to the Food and Drug Administration has been found so that men can enjoy quick comfortable shaves.

PACKAGING

There is a countless variety of packages. For obvious reasons, glass is being displaced by plastic containers, of all shapes and sizes. The use of squeeze bottles, pump sprays, dissolving packages, and the very popular aerosol containers is increasing rapidly. The diversity of sizes of containers, the odd values of content weights, and the difficulty in determining relative values of small and large packages are a continuing problem, not only with chemical products but with practically all packaged products. The whole question is attracting much legislative attention, and "truth in labeling" laws, if given popular support, will probably be enacted in the near future.

COST OF MANUFACTURE OF PRODUCTS

It is instructive to consider the approximate values of a few of the products we regularly purchase. Take as examples a gallon of liquid bleach, a quart of an all-purpose detergent, and a pound of oven cleaner.

LIQUID BLEACH   1 gallon
 5%   Active ingredient   0.4 pound NaOCl @ 15¢/pound = 6¢
95%   Water (note: a pint of water is about 1 pound)
       Container   about 24¢
                                           Cost of product—about 30¢
                                           Retail sales price—about 69¢

ALL-PURPOSE DETERGENT   1 quart
10%   Active ingredient   0.2 pound detergent @ 20¢/pound = 4¢
90%   Water
       Perfume, etc.   about 1¢
       Container   about 15¢
                                           Cost of product—about 20¢
                                           Retail sales price—about 59¢

OVEN CLEANER   1 pound
12%   Sodium hydroxide   0.12 pound @ 3¢/pound = 0.36¢
88%   Water
       Container   about 10¢
                                           Cost of product—about 10.36¢
                                           Retail sales price—about $1.00

You can see that there is a very large markup in these products, and in fact there is a similar markup in most chemical products. The container actually constitutes the most expensive part. Of course, we must take into account the advertising gimmicks, salesmen's commissions, and related expenses. In addition, many of the larger producers divert a portion of the profits to useful research. However, it seems likely that

some enterprising person should be able to bypass the expensive advertising by creating a direct factory-to-consumer outlet or group of outlets
that would allow the buyer to purchase these items at much reduced
prices. There could even be provisions for refill of containers, thus
eliminating even more expense. If such a system could be established,
there would be a merchandising revolution in the chemical product area.
The smaller local manufacturer, who could in this way gain the confidence of the customers without television fanfare, would make very
great gains at the expense of the larger chemical producers while providing the general public with quality products at lower prices. In any
event, the field of household chemical products is a very large and
interesting one and it is hoped that the reader now has a little better
idea about what he is buying, about some of the precautions to observe,
and about the values of the products concerned.

QUESTIONS AND PROJECTS

1. Explain how soap is made and how it performs its cleaning action.

2. Discuss
a. Hydrophilic property
b. Dispersing agent
c. Oil-in-water emulsion
d. Wetting agent
e. Surface tension

3. Compare and give examples of each:
a. Cationics
b. Anionics
c. Nonionics

4. Glycerine is a valuable by-product in the manufacture of soap.
Make a foam ball model of the glycerine molecule.

5. Explain the difference between a colloidal solution and a true
solution. How can a colloidal solution be detected?

6. Write the following as balanced equations:
a. glyceride + sodium hydroxide → glycerine + soap
b. iron (III) oxide + hydrochloric acid → water + iron (III) chloride
c. aluminum metal + sodium hydroxide + water → hydrogen gas +
$Na_3Al(OH)_6$

7. In laundry detergents explain the action of
a. CMC
b. The sunlight ingredient
c. Carbonates, silicates, and phosphates

8. Compile a list of 10 common household cleaners. Indicate
a. Name
b. Retail price per pound
c. Type of package
d. Probable composition
e. An estimate of cost of manufacture

9. Prepare a list of 10 household chemical products that carry a warning on the label. What are the ingredients? Do you think the warnings are adequate?

10. If you were manufacturing and selling the all-purpose detergent for which cost data were given, how many quarts a week would you have to sell to earn $20,000 a year? Ignore overhead.

11. Give examples of products that come in various-size packages and for which the value or price per pound is difficult to ascertain. Should values be made clearer and, if so, how?

12. Find out how many pounds of detergent are sold annually in the United States.

13. Give the formula for
a. Stearic acid
b. Glycerine
c. Sodium hydroxide
d. Sodium carbonate
e. Sodium stearate
f. Ammonium bromide
g. Carbon tetrachloride

14. Explain
a. Micelles
b. Iodophor
c. Primary and secondary layer
d. Hard water
e. Soap versus nonsoap

15. Pour a little milk into a glass of water. Shine a flashlight through the glass in a dark room. Explain what you observe.

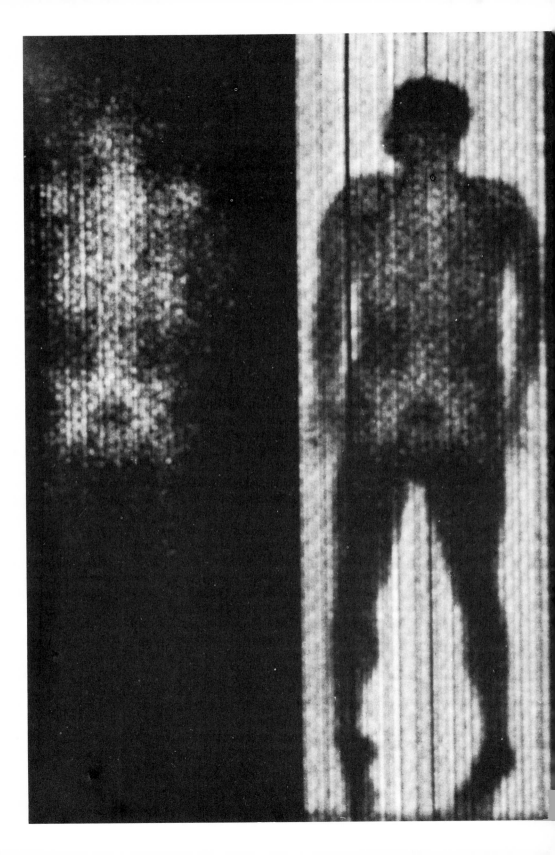

16

NUCLEAR ENERGY AND RADIOCHEMISTRY

At the very beginning of this book we studied the structure of the atom. As you recall, I pointed out that there was a positively charged nucleus, which contained almost all the mass of the atom, surrounded by a number of oppositely charged electrons. In considering the formation of molecules and in fact all the various properties of structures discussed throughout the text, we were concerned only with the electrons and in particular with the outermost electrons. That the electrons should be the chief factor in the combination of atoms is reasonable when we consider the approach of one atom toward another. The electron clouds are going to collide and interact while the nuclei are hidden far inside these clouds.

NUCLEAR STRUCTURE

Why then are the nuclei important at all? Recall first that the nucleus is made up of neutrons and protons. The number of protons determines what the atom is and hence essentially fixes its chemical properties. A nucleus, however, may contain various numbers of neutrons. For instance, ordinary hydrogen has one proton and no neutrons in its nucleus (the neutral atom has one electron around this nucleus). Deuterium, which is also called heavy hydrogen, has one proton and one neutron. These two varieties of hydrogen atoms, which are called isotopes of hydrogen, both exhibit essentially the same chemical properties, such as the formation of water, hydrocarbons, etc. On the other hand, since deuterium is approximately twice as heavy as ordinary hydrogen, its physical properties, such as boiling point and melting point, are somewhat different. Some nuclei are so constituted that they are unstable. In a collection of atoms with unstable nuclei, we observe that a certain proportion constantly undergo decomposition with an accompanying emission of radiation. Such atoms are called *radioactive atoms*, and the study of their chemistry is called *radiochemistry*. When unstable nuclei break down, energy changes are involved, and sometimes energy is released in very large quantities. This energy, which is stored in the nuclei of atoms, is called *nuclear energy*.

The way we have so far described the nucleus would make its study appear to be rather simple. You take a few protons, add a few neutrons, and you have a nucleus. Not so simple! The structure of the nucleus, the various subatomic particles, the energy relationships, the mechanisms of transformations, and many other factors are still not well understood at all. For instance, let's think about the protons with their positive charges. We know that like charges repel, and yet we are going to squeeze these protons so close together that the dimensions are even hard to comprehend. Recall that a baseball constructed of nuclei would weigh ten thousand million tons. Those protons (and neutrons) must really be keeping close company to develop a density like that. Why do the positive charges allow this? Furthermore, the nuclear physicists, in studying reactions of the nucleus, have discovered a large number of subatomic particles (about 100). These they call mesons, baryons, and leptons (not to be confused with leprechauns). For every particle, it is assumed that there is an antiparticle. For instance, the electron with a negative charge is a lepton, while the positron with the same mass but opposite charge is an antilepton. Since all particles exhibit wave motion, we believe that the nucleus is probably held together by some sort of interaction of the wave motions of the principal particles involved. The nuclear forces holding the particles together must, of course, be very powerful. Since the size of the nucleus is extremely small, the wavelengths of the particles must also be very short and their frequencies correspondingly high. High frequency and low wavelength, you recall from our observations at the beach, relate to high energy. We are not surprised, then, that transformations in the nucleus can evolve large energy changes. As for the explanation of the 100 or so particles, it is thought that, inasmuch as there is an energy-mass relationship ($E = mc^2$), many of these particles may be a result of energy exchanges between other particles. In other words, particles may depend upon other particles for their existence. All we need to say is that this is a very stimulating even though complicated topic and that extensive research is continuing in this area. For our purposes it is sufficient to consider that the nucleus is made up of protons and neutrons, and the rest of our discussions will be based upon this simplified, but useful, assumption.

DISCOVERY OF RADIOACTIVITY

Before much was known about the nucleus of the atom, radioactivity was discovered by the French scientist Henri Becquerel. In 1896, he was investigating a uranium ore which fluoresced when exposed to sunlight. It was known that x-rays caused certain materials to fluoresce, and Becquerel wondered if x-rays could be produced by fluorescence. He wrapped a photographic plate in black paper, placed a piece of the ore on top of it, and left it in the sunlight. On developing the plate he found, sure enough, the image of the stone. He set up the same sort of experiment on another day, but after a short exposure, the sun hid behind clouds and he was forced to discontinue the attempt. He placed the plate and the ore in a desk drawer for several days, after which time he decided to develop the plate, even though there had been little exposure to sunlight. Instead of a weak image of the rock, he found a very strong one. Then Becquerel performed another experiment in which he placed the ore on top of the covered plate for a few hours in complete darkness. Again he obtained an image of the specimen. His conclusion was that sunlight and visible fluorescence had nothing to do with the matter. Instead, some sort of penetrating radiation, stronger than ordinary light, was being sent out directly by the ore sample. Not long after, the Curies, in their studies of uranium ores, discovered the element radium.

TYPES OF RADIOACTIVITY

Further studies revealed other naturally occurring radioactive elements. The radiation emitted from the various isotopes was not found to be the same in each case. The principle types of radiation are called *alpha* (α), *beta* (β), and *gamma* (γ). The alpha particle is the nucleus of a helium atom, which contains two protons and two neutrons. The beta particle is an electron that is ejected, as an alpha particle is, at high speed from the decomposing nucleus. The speed of the alpha or beta particles and hence the energy of the radiation depend on the particular isotope that is undergoing decomposition. The gamma ray is electromagnetic radiation, as x-rays are, but has a shorter wavelength and higher frequency. Thus gamma rays are high-energy electromagnetic radiation with great penetrating power. *Radioactive isotopes*, then, are atoms with unstable nuclei.

RADIOACTIVITY DECOMPOSITION RATE

The nuclei are constantly undergoing change and giving off radiation at the same time. The amount of radiation is observed to depend upon the amount of radioactive material present, and the decomposition of nuclei follows a particular pattern. For instance, assume we start with 80 atoms of a radioactive isotope. We observe that 40 atoms decompose in, say, 5 minutes. Continuing our watch we find that 20 more atoms decompose in the next 5 minutes, and that 10 more atoms decompose in the 5-minute period after that. To sum up our observation, we could say that half the atoms present at any moment decompose in the following 5 minutes. We call this time period the *half-life* of this isotope. Some half-lives are fractions of seconds whereas some are millions of years.

It is interesting to observe some of the changes that take place during radioactive decomposition.

SYMBOLS FOR ISOTOPES

Before we look at a few reactions, we should become familiar with the simple notation that is used to indicate the detailed structure of atoms and particles. We said that a nucleus contains protons, their number being the atomic number, and neutrons. The masses of the proton and the neutron are about the same, and the total mass of the nucleus is approximately equal to the sum of the masses of the protons and neutrons. If we assign a mass of one to the proton or neutron, the isotope symbols for ordinary hydrogen and deuterium become the following:

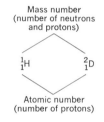

Mass number
(number of neutrons
and protons)

$^{1}_{1}H$ $^{2}_{1}D$

Atomic number
(number of protons)

Ordinary hydrogen   Deuterium

Since the *mass number* is the sum of the protons and neutrons, we have only to subtract the atomic number from the mass number to get the number of neutrons. For instance, there are no neutrons in ordinary hydrogen $(1 - 1)$ and there is one neutron in deuterium $(2 - 1)$.

There is still another isotope of hydrogen, and this one, which is called tritium, is radioactive. The symbol is as follows:

$$^{3}_{1}T$$

Tritium

You can easily see that there are two neutrons in this particular isotope of hydrogen. The following are the symbols for the helium atom and the alpha particle:

$$^4_2He \qquad ^4_2He^{++}$$

Neutral   Alpha particle
helium atom   (helium atom
without electrons)

Notice that the alpha particle is just the helium nucleus without the two surrounding electrons. This is indicated by the two superscript pluses. A beta particle, which is very small compared to a proton or neutron, is assigned a mass of zero. Since it has a negative unit charge we indicate a minus one where we ordinarily place the atomic number. Therefore the symbol for the beta particle (or an electron) becomes:

$$^0_{-1}e$$

Beta particle

EQUATIONS FOR NUCLEAR REACTIONS

Now we are ready to write equations illustrating a few types of radioactive decomposition.

$$^{238}_{92}U \longrightarrow {}^4_2He^{++} + {}^{234}_{90}Th$$

ALPHA DECAY

The above is an example of alpha decay. The uranium atom has lost from its nucleus two protons and two neutrons. Having lost protons, the atom is no longer uranium, with that element's characteristic properties, but is now thorium, with an atomic number of 90. Since a mass of four was lost, the new thorium atom has a mass of 234 (238 − 4). Notice in the equation that the superscripts on the right add up to the superscript on the left. The same is true of the subscripts. During such a reaction the outer electrons redistribute themselves. In the reaction above we can consider that two outer electrons leave each decomposing uranium atom and eventually find their way to the positively charged alpha particle.

$$^{14}_{6}C \longrightarrow ^{\ 0}_{-1}e + ^{14}_{7}N$$

BETA DECAY

In this example an isotope of carbon changes into an isotope of nitrogen with the emission of a beta particle. We can interpret the gain of a proton and the ejection of an electron as the result of the conversion of a neutron into a proton and an electron.

GAMMA DECAY

Since this type of decay involves no change in atomic number or mass number, there is really no point in writing an equation. The atom is dropping from an excited state to a lower energy level with the emission of energy in the form of a gamma ray.

DETECTING AND MEASURING RADIOACTIVITY

Now that we know what radioactivity is and what the principle types of radiation are, let us survey the kinds of instruments used for detection and measurement. All radiation is capable of removing electrons from matter as it interacts with the matter. Ions are produced as electrons are removed from struck molecules. The measurement of this ionization by chemical and electronic means is the basis for the detecting and measuring of radiation.

IONIZATION CHAMBERS

Measurement of a current in a tube containing a gas can indicate the intensity of rays passing through such a tube. The rays produce ionization, thus changing the electrical conductivity, which in turn changes the current that can flow between two charged plates in the tube. The amount of current is a measure of the amount of ionization produced by the radiation. This sort of instrument is effective for only relatively high-intensity radiation.

GEIGER COUNTER

The Geiger counter uses a Geiger-Müller tube, which is a modification of the ionization chamber and is capable of counting the *number* of ionizing rays that pass through per unit time (but is not capable of measuring their energy). The counter is applicable to radiations over a wide range of energies. The tube is filled with gas and contains two electrodes with a very high voltage difference between them. Any incident radiation that starts ionization of the gas causes a momentary short circuit in the tube. This can be recorded as a flash of light, a click, or a number on a scale. It should be pointed out that alpha particles have a very short range and can be stopped by a sheet of paper; beta particles have a longer range but can be stopped by thin sheets of metal; whereas gamma rays can only be halted by thick layers of dense material, such as concrete or lead. The varying degrees of penetration make possible the detection of each with the Geiger tube. For instance, with a tube having a fairly thick wall, only gamma rays can pass through and be counted. Thinner walls will transmit gamma and beta rays but will absorb alpha particles. To measure gamma rays in the presence of beta rays, a thin metal shield can be placed in front of the tube. The shield absorbs the beta particles but transmits the gamma rays.

SCINTILLATION COUNTERS

Certain substances give off light when they are struck by radiation. These light flashes can be counted electronically by a scintillation counter. This instrument is widely used mainly because of its superiority to the Geiger counter in measuring low-energy radiations.

ELECTROSCOPES

The principle involved in electroscopic measurement of radiation is the same as in the familiar gold-leaf electroscope, where two gold leaves are given a charge. The leaves repel one another and stay apart for some time unless something comes along to neutralize the charge. In the various electroscopes it is commonly a metallized quartz fiber that is given the charge. The degree to which ionizing radiation discharges the fiber can be read on a scale. A small electroscope in the shape of a pen is called a *dosimeter,* and is worn by personnel who may be exposed to radiation. The dosimeter can be held up to the eye and read at any time.

PHOTOGRAPHIC FILM

The discovery made by Becquerel is still used in a practical way. This is mainly employed in the form of a badge which bears a number corresponding to the worker who may become exposed to radiation during the course of his day's work. Unlike the dosimeter, the film badge must be developed and compared to a standard before the extent of radiation exposure can be determined.

CLOUD AND BUBBLE CHAMBERS

A unique visual demonstration of the presence and path of radiation is afforded by a cloud or bubble chamber, the former for weaker particles, the latter for high-energy particles. A cloud chamber contains moist air which is chilled, usually with dry ice. The moisture is just on the verge of condensing. When an ionizing particle enters the chamber, it strikes air molecules removing electrons along its path. The ions so produced act as nuclei on which condensation takes place and a tiny vapor trail is observed for each particle. In the bubble chamber, liquid hydrogen is usually used in place of moist air. This denser medium slows down more energetic particles which pass quickly through an ordinary cloud chamber without causing many collisions. When the pressure on the hydrogen is slightly reduced, bubbles appear along the track of the particle.

RADIATION HAZARDS

Since we are talking about protecting persons from radiation we should have some idea of the relative hazards involved. Obviously, alpha particles which can be stopped by a piece of paper present no external hazard. The outer surface of the skin stops these. Beta particles, depending upon their velocity, can penetrate up to about a third of an inch of body tissue. Gamma rays, because of their great penetrating power, are, of course, the greatest problem.

Notice that the word "external" was used above. An alpha- or beta-emitting atom, which may present little external hazard, is extremely harmful within the body. The continuing local radiation produces ionization and structural rearrangement that can even produce lasting genetic changes. (This is why radioactive air pollution is so serious.)

NUCLEAR STABILITY

We should consider for a moment what reasons if any can be found for radioactivity. Why are some nuclei more stable than others and why are certain products obtained in nuclear reactions? As I have already pointed out, the exact structure and nature of the nucleus are not very clear. However, certain gross observations lead to useful generalizations.

NEUTRON-TO-PROTON RATIO

For example, the neutron-to-proton ratio of the various elements is related to their stability. For about the first 18 elements there are equal numbers of neutrons and protons. This ratio increases to a maximum of about 1.6 for the heaviest stable nuclei. As for the occurrence in nature of stable isotopes, it has been found that relatively few are found with a neutron-to-proton ratio greater than 1.2, the value which occurs at the element of atomic number 31 (gallium). Supporting evidence is found in the fact that the 20 most abundant elements occur among the first 40 elements.

BINDING ENERGY

Another guiding principle is in terms of the *binding energy*. It is observed that the mass of the nucleus of an atom does not correspond exactly to the sum of the masses of its component parts. This difference in mass corresponds to a particular amount of energy through the energy-mass relationship $E = mc^2$. We may consider that this amount of energy is

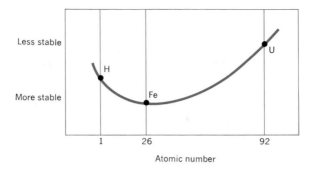

FIGURE 16–1

liberated when the atom is put together. We call it the *binding energy*. Just as a stone rolls down a hill, loses energy, and arrives at a lower energy level, a more stable location, so when an atom is synthesized from its component parts, it loses energy and arrives at a more stable situation. The atoms that lose the most energy reach the lowest energy level, whereas others, which lose less energy, are at higher levels. The way it works out for various atoms is shown in Fig. 16–1. If you think of the curve as the profile of a valley, you can get a simple picture of the relative stability of the various elements.

The elements with atomic numbers close to iron (26) have lost the most mass (energy) per nucleon in formation and are thus the most stable elements. Others, such as hydrogen and uranium, have not lost as much mass per nucleon and are thus higher up on the hillsides. You might suspect that, like stones rolling downhill, such atoms as uranium and hydrogen will tend to "roll downhill" by changing into atoms with atomic numbers closer to iron. This is indeed what happens. Various types of nuclear reactions take place, generally resulting in atoms with greater binding energies. As we look at some other nuclear reactions we can refer back to this chart to verify our observations.

OTHER NUCLEAR REACTIONS

So far we have considered only nuclear decompositions in naturally occurring radioactive isotopes. Actually, other sorts of nuclear reactions are possible. Using instruments such as cyclotrons, betatrons, bev-

FIGURE 16–2   THE BEVATRON AT BERKELEY IN ITS SHIELDING OF CONCRETE. *(BY PERMISSION OF LAWRENCE RADIATION LABORATORY, UNI-VERSITY OF CALIFORNIA.)*

atrons, and synchrotrons, scientists can shoot particles such as electrons and protons at various targets. The particles enter the nuclei of the target material, causing various reactions to take place. Both stable and radioactive isotopes can result, accompanied by various types of radiation. Energy can be released in small or very large quantities, depending upon the particular reaction. As for the production of isotopes, the elements beyond uranium, called the transuranic elements, which were not found in nature and which were predicted to be nonexistent, were synthesized by nuclear reactions. For instance, a neutron fired into a uranium atom produces gamma radiation and an unstable isotope of uranium.

$$^{238}_{92}U + ^{1}_{0}n \longrightarrow ^{239}_{92}U + \gamma$$

Uranium 238   Uranium 239

This unstable isotope decomposes by beta decay to a new element, atomic number 93, called neptunium.

$$^{239}_{92}\text{U} \longrightarrow \,^{239}_{93}\text{Np} + \,^{0}_{-1}\text{e}$$

Uranium 239   Neptunium

This isotope in turn decomposes to atomic number 94, plutonium.

$$^{239}_{93}\text{Np} \longrightarrow \,^{239}_{94}\text{Pu} + \,^{0}_{-1}\text{e} + \gamma$$

Neptunium   Plutonium

Many other isotopes, both stable and radioactive, are produced routinely through nuclear reactions. Some of these isotopes are very valuable in research and in medicine.

FISSION REACTIONS

Certain nuclear reactions result in the release of vast amounts of energy. One such reaction is called *fission*. For example, when a uranium isotope of mass 235 is struck by a slow-moving neutron, it captures the neutron, becomes unstable, and breaks up into two lighter atoms, while releasing two or three neutrons.

$$^{235}_{92}\text{U} + \,^{1}_{0}\text{n} \longrightarrow \,^{236}_{92}\text{U} \qquad\qquad ^{236}_{92}\text{U} \longrightarrow \,^{144}_{56}\text{Ba} + \,^{90}_{36}\text{Kr} + \,^{1}_{0}\text{n} + \,^{1}_{0}\text{n}$$

Uranium 235   Uranium 236

The released neutrons can then strike other uranium atoms to continue and multiply the reaction. The mass of the products is significantly less than the mass of the starting material, corresponding to the release of a very large amount of energy. If this chain reaction can be controlled so that it continues at a steady rate and delivers energy uniformly, the system is called a nuclear reactor. Such reactors are now commonly used in ships, in submarines, and in the production of electrical power.

FUSION REACTIONS

Another type of nuclear reaction that produces excessive energy is called the fusion reaction. The source of energy in the stars, including our own sun, has been a mystery for centuries. Great gobs of energy are constantly released without a significant lowering of temperature. Since reactions involving the fusing or squeezing together of nuclei have been demonstrated, present-day scientists believe that it is this sort of reaction that takes place in the stars. For instance, the following equation could be representative:

$$^2_1D \ + \ ^2_1D \ \longrightarrow \ ^4_2He \ + \ \text{Energy}$$

There is actually a very significant difference in mass between the products and the reactants; this mass loss corresponds, as in the fission process, to a large amount of energy. Such a reaction as this, where nuclei are being squashed together, requires the very high temperatures which exist on the stars. It has not yet been possible to arrange the

FIGURE 16–3   CURRENT RESEARCH TOWARDS CONTROLLING NUCLEAR FUSION. WITHIN THE HOLLOW, DOUGHNUT-SHAPED CHAMBER OF THIS MACHINE, NUCLEI WOULD BE HELD IN ORBIT BY MAGNETIC FORCES. THEY COULD THEN BE HEATED TO STELLAR TEMPERATURES WITHOUT MELTING EVERYTHING AROUND. (BY PERMISSION OF PRINCETON UNIVERSITY.)

proper conditions of temperature and pressure so that the fusion reaction can be conducted in a controlled fashion. Extensive research is now under way to find a solution to this problem, a solution which could mean almost unlimited power for peaceful purposes. Notice in Fig. 16–1 that in both fission and fusion reactions the reactants, uranium atoms or deuterium atoms, are "running downhill" toward the bottom of the valley where the atoms have more binding energy and are thus more stable.

Probably the most promising and most valuable application of fusion reactions is the nuclear reactor. As the earth runs out of fossil fuel, we must certainly look to other sources for power, and nuclear energy seems to be the solution.

TRACERS

Both in chemical research and in medicine the use of tracers is of very great importance. As we know, the chemical properties of an element are determined by the electrons surrounding the nucleus. If we mix a radioactive isotope of an element in with stable isotopes of the same element, it will be carried along and behave just like the other atoms. However, its location and concentration can be easily measured by our detection instruments. Thus, a reaction or an ailment involving a particular element can be studied in detail by introducing a radioactive tracer. It should be mentioned that isotopes other than radioactive ones can be used in the same manner. For instance, deuterium, which is not radioactive but which has different properties than ordinary hydrogen, is frequently used to gain information about hydrogen-containing compounds. An interesting example of the scientific use of a tracer is the determination of the age of remains of animal and plant life. There is a certain small percentage of a radioactive isotope of carbon, $^{14}_{6}C$, in the air which we breathe. During life, animals and plants assimilate this carbon into their structure and maintain it at a certain constant level. After death, however, the isotope is no longer taken in, and what was already in the body decays and gradually diminishes. Since we know the half-life of this isotope and can measure how much is currently present in the remains, the time of death and hence the age can easily be calculated.

CANCER THERAPY

The effect of radiation on body tissue is a selective one. In particular it attacks young and fast-growing cancer cells more readily than normal cells. For this reason, radioactive isotopes such as radium, cobalt, chlorine, and iodine are frequently used in medicine.

If the radiation of an isotope such as cobalt 60 is carefully focused on a diseased area, the cancerous cells can be destroyed with a minimum of damage to the normal cells. Internal application is also employed, as in the study of the thyroid gland with radioactive iodine.

OTHER APPLICATIONS

There are many other common uses of radioactivity in addition to those described above. Some of these are the study of fertilizer uptake by plants, plant nutrition, food preservation, controlling the thickness of a continuous strip of plastic or other material, insect control, "x-rays" of welds and castings, wear and lubrication tests, and many others. Whether civilization will proceed in a useful or in a destructive direction depends to a large extent upon the use or misuse of nuclear energy.

QUESTIONS AND PROJECTS

1. Write isotope symbols for
a. Deuterium
b. Uranium of mass 239
c. Polonium of mass 218
d. Bismuth of mass 214
e. Lead of mass 206

2. Write equations for the following nuclear transformations:
a. Thorium (mass 234) → beta particle + ?
b. Polonium (mass 214) → alpha particle + ?
c. Fluorine (mass 20) → beta particle + ?
d. Beryllium (mass 9) + proton → alpha particle + ?

3. An isotope has a half-life of ten minutes. If we start with 20,000 atoms, how many will remain at the end of 30 minutes?

4. Compare alpha, beta, and gamma radiation.

5. Discuss methods for detecting and recording radiation.

6. Discuss the hazards of alpha, beta, and gamma radiation with respect to external and internal exposure. Why is it important for an x-ray technician or radiation therapist to keep track of his or her total exposure? How careful should the average person be as to annual x-ray dosage for chest, teeth, and other parts of the body?

7. Write a short description of the construction and operation of a nuclear accelerator.

8. How can a transuranium element be produced? Give an example.

9. Compare fission and fusion reactions. Give examples and explain why large amounts of energy are liberated.

10. Report on one of the following:
a. The use of a tracer in a medical problem
b. Industrial radiography
c. Determining the age of a fossil

11. Element 104 has recently been produced. Report on it.

12. Explain what is meant by binding energy. Which elements have the most? Which the least?

13. Give the mass numbers of
a. The isotope of zirconium that has 51 neutrons
b. Deuterium
c. Alpha particle
d. An electron
e. The isotope of uranium that has 146 neutrons

14. Discuss Becquerel's discovery of radioactivity.

15. Explain the operation of a nuclear reactor.

GLOSSARY

ACID A chemical substance which produces hydrogen ions in water solution. HCl and H_2SO_4 are examples.

AEROBIC DEGRADATION The breaking down of substances by bacteria that utilize oxygen.

AEROSOL A colloidal solution in which a substance is dispersed in a gas.

AGRONOMIST A scientist who studies the use of land for production of food.

ALGAE Very small plants that generally live in water.

ALKALI A chemical substance that usually produces hydroxyl ions in water solution; a base. Sodium hydroxide, NaOH, is an example.

ALPHA PARTICLE The helium atom without its two electrons (the helium nucleus).

ANAEROBIC DEGRADATION The breaking down of substances by bacteria that do not utilize oxygen.

ANION An ion with a negative charge.

ANTIOXIDANT   A substance that prevents reaction of another material with oxygen.

AQUIFER   An underground reservoir of water.

ASTHMA   A disease involving constriction of the breathing passages.

ATACTIC POLYMER   A polymer with side chains randomly arranged on the main chains.

ATOM   The smallest subdivision of an element having the properties of that element and able to take part in chemical reactions.

ATOMIC ABSORPTION   The assimilation by an element of light characteristic of that element. It forms the basis for a modern method of chemical analysis.

BACTERICIDE   A substance capable of killing bacteria.

BETA PARTICLE   An electron emitted at high speed from the nuclei of radioactive elements.

BETATRON   A nuclear accelerator which drives electrons at very high speeds into a target.

BEVATRON   An accelerator which can drive protons at extremely high speeds.

BINARY   Made up of two parts.

BINARY COMPOUND   A compound made up of two elements.

BINDING ENERGY   A measure of the nuclear stability of an atom calculated by comparing the mass of the atom with the mass of its components.

BIOCHEMICAL OXYGEN DEMAND (BOD)   The amount of oxygen needed by microorganisms for aerobic degradation of a certain amount of degradable material.

BIODEGRADABLE   Capable of being decomposed by living organisms.

BRONCHITIS   Inflammation of the air passages from the trachea to the lungs.

CARCINOGEN   An agent capable of producing cancer.

CATALYST   A substance which can speed or slow a reaction without itself being consumed.

CATION   An atom or group of atoms which has more protons than electrons and hence a positive charge.

CHELATION   The reaction of a molecule or ion with a metal ion wherein more than one bond to the metal ion is formed at the same time.

COLLOID   A solution wherein the dissolved particles are much larger than the molecular size found in true solutions. The particles, however, are not large enough to settle out under the influence of gravity.

COLORIMETRIC ANALYSIS   A method of analysis which depends upon the color produced in a specific chemical reaction. Measurement of the depth of the color can give an accurate determination of the amount of a substance under study.

COMPOUND   A substance formed by reaction of two or more elements.

COPOLYMER   A polymer formed from two or more different monomers.

COVALENCE   A type of chemical bonding brought about by the sharing of electrons between atoms.

CROSS-LINK   A bond formed between polymer chains.

CRYSTALLINE   Having a very regular three-dimensional arrangement of atoms, molecules, or ions.

CYCLOTRON   An instrument which accelerates charged particles in ever-increasing circular paths until they are allowed to strike a target. Various nuclear reactions can be brought about with this apparatus.

DEGRADATION   The breaking down of a chemical structure.

DESALINATION   The removal of salts. In particular, the removal of salt from sea water to produce fresh water.

DETERGENT   A surface-active agent, with or without additives, that can produce a cleaning action.

DEUTERIUM   An isotope of hydrogen which consists of an external electron and a nucleus containing one proton and one neutron.

DIATOMIC   Consisting of two atoms. For instance, H_2 is a diatomic molecule.

DIMER   A combination of two units of monomer. A TRIMER contains three units, etc.

DISINFECTANT   A chemical that has the ability to kill a wide range of microorganisms.

DISPERSANT   An agent which helps distribute a substance in another medium.

DISTILLATION   A physical process wherein substances are separated from one another by virtue of their different boiling points. For instance, the distillation of sea water leaves behind the dissolved salts.

EDEMA, PULMONARY   Swelling of the lung cells.

ELECTRODIALYSIS   A process wherein ions are electrostatically attracted out of a solution.

ELECTROMAGNETIC RADIATION   A combination of pulsating electric and magnetic fields traveling at high speed. Of the large number of possible frequencies and wavelengths, only one narrow band can be detected by the human eye. This we know as visible light.

ELECTRON   A subatomic particle with a single negative charge and a mass 1/1836 the mass of the proton.

ELECTRONEGATIVE   Tending to attract electrons.

ELECTROPOSITIVE   Tending to lose electrons.

ELECTROSCOPE   An instrument which measures electrostatic charge.

ELECTROSTATIC PRECIPITATOR   A device installed in smokestacks to remove soot and other particulates.

EMPHYSEMA   An incurable lung disease usually observed in persons who are smokers or who are exposed to severe air pollution.

EMULSIFYING AGENT   A chemical that helps the formation of an emulsion.

EMULSION   A colloidal solution wherein the dispersed substance and the dispersing medium are both liquids.

ENDOTHERMIC   Absorbing energy; said of reactions.

ENTOMOLOGIST   A scientist who studies insects.

ESTER   A substance yielded by the reaction of an alcohol and an acid. The process is called ESTERIFICATION.

EXOTHERMIC   Liberating energy; said of reactions.

FALLOPIAN TUBE   One of two passageways in the female through which the egg passes from the ovary into the uterus.

FISSION   A nuclear reaction which results in the splitting of larger atoms with a simultaneous release of energy.

FREQUENCY   The number of pulses per unit time in a regular, pulsating occurrence.

FUNGICIDE   A chemical capable of killing various fungi.

FUSION   A nuclear reaction that involves the fusing together of small nuclei with the simultaneous release of large amounts of energy.

GAMMA RADIATION   A portion of the electromagnetic spectrum having very high frequency and therefore high energy.

GEIGER COUNTER   An instrument for measuring the amount of various ionizing radiations.

GLYCERINE   An alcohol containing three functional groups:

$$
\begin{array}{c}
\text{H} \\
\text{H C}\!-\!\text{OH} \\
| \\
\text{H C} \quad \text{OH} \\
| \\
\text{H C}\!-\!\text{OH} \\
\text{H}
\end{array}
$$

Glycerine

The triesters of this alcohol formed by reaction with various acids are GLYCERIDES.

GROWTH REGULATOR   In agricultural chemistry, a chemical which can influence the growth of a plant.

HALF-LIFE   The length of time in which, in a group of radioactive atoms, half the atoms decompose.

HORMONES   Chemical structures which are produced by the endocrine glands and which regulate various operations in the body.

HYBRID ORBITALS   Atomic orbitals formed from ground-state orbitals. They are brought about under the influence of a chemical reaction to produce a more stable structure than would be possible otherwise.

HYDROCARBON   A compound made up of carbon and hydrogen only.

HYDROLOGICAL CYCLE   The itinerary of water on earth, including rainfall, evaporation, melting, transportation, and underground and surface movement.

HYDROPHILIC   "Water-loving"; water-seeking.

HYDROPHOBIC   "Water-fearing"; water-repelling.

INFRARED   Occurring near the red end of the visible spectrum; said of electromagnetic radiation. Heat radiation is in the infrared range.

INORGANIC   Generally, *not* containing carbon.

INSECTICIDE   A chemical capable of killing various insects.

INVERSION   A meteorological condition wherein a warm blanket of air covers a cold blanket.

IODOPHOR   A compound in which iodine molecules are bonded. The iodine is easily released to perform its disinfecting duties.

ION   An atom or group of atoms which has an electrostatic charge. A cation has a positive charge, and an anion has a negative charge.

IONIZATION CHAMBER   An instrument which measures high-intensity radiation by changes in an electric current in a gas-filled tube. The radiation produces ionization of the gas and thus changes the current passing through the tube.

ISOTACTIC   Containing side chains that are regularly arranged along one side of the main chain.

ISOTOPES   Atoms of the same element that have different numbers of neutrons in the nucleus.

LATENT HEAT OF VAPORIZATION   The amount of heat necessary to convert a liquid into the gaseous state.

LATTICE   The regular three-dimensional arrangement found in crystals.

LEPTON   One of a class of light subatomic particles. The electron belongs to this class.

LIMNOLOGY   The study of fresh waters.

LYE   A strong base, such as sodium hydroxide (NaOH)

MASS   The amount of matter in a body. This can be measured by the force of gravity acting on it.

MESON   A subatomic particle with a mass between that of an electron and that of a proton.

MICELLES   Groups of molecules or ions consisting of the dispersed substance in a colloidal solution.

MOLECULAR ORBITAL (MO) THEORY   A theory of chemical bonding which states that there are series of orbitals belonging to the molecule as a whole, just as an atom has a series of atomic orbitals.

MOLECULE   A combination of two or more atoms held together by covalent bonds. Chlorine, Cl_2, and water, H_2O, are molecules.

MONATOMIC   Consisting of one atom only.

MONOMERS   The building blocks of polymers. The monomer molecules react with each other to form chains of varying lengths.

NEUTRALIZATION   The reaction of an acid and a base to form water and a salt.

NEUTRON   A subatomic particle which has a mass of one and has no electrostatic charge.

NONIONIC   Not containing ions.

NUCLEUS   The central portion of an atom, where almost all its mass is situated.

ORBITAL   The volume of space which represents the net location of a particular electron.

ORGANIC   Containing carbon.

OVULATION   The production or discharge of an egg.

OXIDATION   A reaction which increases the oxidation state (see below) of an element—frequently a reaction with oxygen.

OXIDATION STATE   A number (possibly zero) indicating the extent to which an element has lost or gained electrons or has lost or gained a share in electrons.

pH   A measure of the amount of active acidity in a solution. Neutral solutions have a pH of 7, acids less than 7, and bases greater than 7.

PHOTOCHEMICAL   Said of a chemical reaction in which light is a factor.

PHOTOMETER   An instrument for measuring light.

PI BOND   A covalent bond in which the orbital overlap does not occur on the axis between the atoms.

PLANT PATHOLOGIST   A scientist who studies the diseases of plants.

PLANT PHYSIOLOGIST   A scientist who studies plant processes and the functions of the various plant parts.

PLASTICIZER   A chemical which is added to a polymer to yield flexibility.

POLAR   Having a separation between positive and negative charge.

POLYATOMIC   Consisting of two or more atoms. For example, $SO_4^=$ is a polyatomic ion.

POLYMER   A substance yielded by the reaction of two or more units of a monomer.

PROBABILITY DENSITY   A mathematical term that tells the relative amount of time an electron spends in a particular volume of space.

PROTON   A subatomic particle of mass one and having a charge of plus one.

PROTOZOA   Very tiny animal life usually found in water.

QUATERNARY COMPOUND (QUAT)   An ionic compound in which four carbon-containing groups are attached to a nitrogen atom. For example, replacing the four hydrogens in ammonium chloride ($NH_4^+Cl^-$) with organic radicals yields a quat.

RADIATION   Short form for electromagnetic radiation; or, in radioactivity, the emitting of electromagnetic radiation or particles from unstable nuclei.

RADIOACTIVE   Said of an element whose nuclei undergo spontaneous decomposition.

RADIOACTIVITY   The process through which unstable nuclei decompose into other elements with attendant release of radiation.

SCINTILLATION COUNTER   An instrument that measures radioactivity by light flashes produced in a phosphorescent material.

SHELL   In atomic structure, the electrons are located in various shells surrounding the nucleus. There is one shell for each principal quantum number, with the shells increasing in size and electron capacity as the number increases.

SIGMA BOND   A covalent bond in which the orbital overlap occurs on the axis between the atoms.

SMOG   A name for air pollution, derived from the words "smoke" and "fog."

SOAP   The sodium or potassium salt of a long-chain acid. A glyceride plus sodium or potassium hydroxide yields soap and the by-product glycerine. Other detergents are nonsoaps.

SOLVENT   The medium in which something (the solute) is dissolved. For example, water is a solvent for sugar.

SPECTROGRAM   A graph which records the results of a chemical analysis carried out with infrared, visible, or ultraviolet light.

SPECTROPHOTOMETER   An electronic instrument which measures the amount of light of various wavelengths absorbed by a chemical sample.

SPECTROSCOPE   An instrument for visually observing the composition of light. The light is generally passed through a prism which separates it into its different wavelengths.

SPECTROSCOPY   The observation, recording, and interpretation of all types of spectra.

SUBSHELL   In atomic structure, the major shells are composed of subshells which in turn are made up of orbitals. The number of subshells in a major shell is the same as the number of the major shell. For example, in the second shell there are two subshells, the 2s and the 2p.

SURFACE-ACTIVE AGENT   A chemical which has the property of affecting the surface tension (see below) of liquids.

SURFACE TENSION   A property of liquids which measures the molecules' attraction to one another and their resistance to being attached to anything else.

SUSPENDING AGENT   A chemical which is capable of suspending one substance in another.

SUSPENSION   Generally, a liquid in which solid particles are dispersed. The suspended particles are quite large compared to molecular size and usually settle out under the influence of gravity.

SYNCHROTRON   An instrument which accelerates particles to extremely high energies.

SYNDIOTACTIC POLYMER   A polymer with side chains alternately arranged on either side of the principal chain.

SYNERGIST   A chemical which helps another chemical to produce an effect.

SYNTHESIS A series of reactions of various chemicals to produce a desired end product. A synthesis may have many steps or only one.

THERMOPLASTIC Having the property of melting when heated and then reforming when cooled.

THERMOSETTING Having the property of decomposing when heated.

TOXICITY The poisonous property of a substance.

TOXIN A poisonous substance produced by a plant or animal, particularly by the action of bacteria on food or in an animal.

TRACER A radioactive element introduced into a system for the purpose of tracing the path of that element.

TRACHEA In animals, the windpipe, which leads down the neck into the bronchi.

TRANSPIRATION The process whereby plants give off water vapor to the atmosphere.

ULTRAVIOLET Being in the portion of the electromagnetic spectrum that has frequencies somewhat higher than the violet end of the visible spectrum.

UNSATURATED Said of carbon compounds that have double or triple covalent bonds between carbon atoms.

VALENCE The overall combining power of an atom. Valence, unlike oxidation number, does not indicate the positive or negative nature of the bonded atom.

VALENCE BOND The theory that considers bonds to be a result of interaction of individual atomic orbitals.

VIRUCIDE A chemical capable of killing viruses.

VISCOSITY A measure of a liquid's ability to flow.

WAVELENGTH The distance between pulses in a periodic event.

WETTING AGENT A chemical which has the ability to get a liquid to stick to a solid.

X-RAY Electromagnetic radiation of high frequency and hence high energy.

APPENDIX

LABORATORY

Many introductory nonmajor chemistry courses include a laboratory session. Indeed, many instructors believe that the true feeling for an experimental science such as chemistry is lost without experience in the laboratory. Suitable experiments to accompany the present text can be found in the following manual:

Frantz and Malm, *Fundamental Experiments for College Chemistry.*

FOAM BALL MODELS

Included in the Questions and Projects at the end of each chapter are a number of assignments concerning the construction of simple models of various structures. The student who has to put such models together usually gains special involvement and insight which are not obtainable by simply inspecting a completed model or picture of a model. In fact, it has been found very beneficial to have each lecture student bring to class a simple construction kit and make models right along with the instructor.

If your book store does not have such a kit available, a suitable inexpensive one is available from:

Dennis Chemical Models, P.O. Box 43, Short Beach, Conn.

OVERHEAD PROJECTOR AND OVERHEAD PROJECTUALS

The author has found the overhead projector to be very useful in chemistry lectures. The projector is mounted either on the lecture desk or on a wagon near the lecture desk. The instructor faces the students as he writes or places prepared projectuals on the instrument. Another overhead projector mounted horizontally can be set off to one side to be used for projecting micro or semimicro demonstrations. The instructor still has the blackboard for additional notes. The projector on which the instructor writes can be provided with a roll of sheet plastic which can be cranked to expose a fresh surface as needed. If water color pencils are used, the rolls can be washed and reused many times.

Prepared chemistry projectuals, either in color or black and white, can be purchased. Some of these have sequential overlays which provide interesting presentations. Sources are listed below:

General Aniline and Film Corp., Audio Visual, Binghamton, N.Y.

United Transparencies, Inc., P.O. Box 888, Binghamton, N.Y.

Tecnifax Corp., Holyoke, Mass.

Minnesota Mining and Manufacturing Company, Visual Products Div., 3M Center, St. Paul, Minn. 55101

Some instructors prefer to prepare their own projectuals. This can easily be done. Certain copying machines, such as those made by Minnesota Mining and Manufacturing Company, make transparencies directly from a picture or drawing. These can then be mounted on a frame for permanency. A book containing a large number of good line drawings for this purpose can be obtained from:

Keuffel & Esser Co., Audiovisual Division, So. Hoboken, N.J.

For detailed description of chemistry experiments that can be performed on the overhead projector, the following guide by Dr. Hubert N. Alyea is available:

Tested Demonstrations in Chemistry, Journal of Chemical Education, Easton, Pa.

FILMS

Short films that can present topics, equipment, or applications that would be difficult to describe in the ordinary lecture are finding increased acceptance. There are many excellent films that do not eat deeply into lecture time, and for this type of course such films are particularly useful. Most of the films are free, while others can be rented for a small fee. In either case, reservations should be made well in advance. Below are listed the film sources and a number of recommended films and the chapters with which they can be shown. Running times are approximate.

FILM SOURCES

ACS—American Cancer Society—Local Office

BTC—Bell Telephone—Local Office

Chem/MLA—Chem Study Films, available from Modern Learning Aids, 1212 Avenue of the Americas, New York, N.Y. 10036

EBF—Encyclopedia Britannica Films, Inc., 1150 Wilmette Ave., Wilmette, Ill. 60091

IU—Indiana University, Audio Visual Center, Bloomington, Ind.

MCA—Manufacturing Chemists Association, 1825 Connecticut Ave., N.W., Washington, D.C. 20009

PHS—Public Health Service, National Medical Audiovisual Center (Annex), Chamblee, Ga. 30005

FILM TITLE	SOURCE	USE WITH CHAPTER
Sources of Air Pollution (10 min)	PHS	14
Effects of Air Pollution (10 min)	PHS	14
Physical Chemistry of Polymers (25 min)	BTC	10, 11
Introducing Chemistry: How Atoms Combine (11 min)	IU	4
Ill Winds on a Sunny Day (20 min)	PHS	14
The Embattled Cell (21 min)	ACS	14
Cracking the Code of Life (22 min)	ACS	8
The Hydrogen Atom—As Viewed by Quantum Mechanics (13 min)	Chem/MLA	2
Vitamins and Your Health (17 min)	MCA	12
Modern Miracle Makers (13 min)	MCA	7
To Save Your Life (8 min)	MCA	7, 8
Colloids (11 min)	MCA	15
Atomic Energy (11 min)	EBF	16
Focus on Foam (20 min)	MCA	10, 11
Ten Thousand to One (17 min)	MCA	7, 9
Chemical Families (14 min)	Chem/MLA	3

INDEX

Water:
    in polymer formation, 104
    sources, 150–151
    structure, 145–146
Wave equations, 11
Wave motion, 9–12

Wavelength, 9
Wetting agent, 185

Zinc, 20
Zoologist, 88